Teacher Edition

Grade 5

Houghton Mifflin Harcourt

Getting Ready for **High-Stakes Assessments**

INCLUDES:

- Benchmark Tests
- Performance Assessment Tasks
- Test Taking Strategies
- Standards Practice
- Answer Keys and Scoring Rubrics
- Student Record Forms, with Prescriptions

Printed in the U.S.A.

ISBN 978-0-544-60570-1

4 5 6 7 8 9 10 0304 22 21 20 19 18 17 16

4500603000 B C D E F G

Contents

Overview of *Getting Ready for High-Stakes Assessments*

How Assessment Can Help Individualize Instruction

The *Getting Ready for High-Stakes Assessments* contains different types of assessment for use throughout the school year. The following pages will explain how these assessments can be utilized to diagnose students' understanding of the Common Core State Standards and to guide instructional choices, improve students' performance, and to help facilitate their mastery of math content.

Diagnostic Assessment

Beginning-of-Year Test contains items that are presented in the various high-stakes assessments. This test should be utilized early in the year to establish on-grade level skills that students may already understand. This benchmark test will facilitate customization of instructional content to optimize the time spent teaching specific objectives.

Formative Assessment

Using the results of the **Middle-of-Year Test** will gauge student progress and help target opportunities for instructional adjustments, as required.

Summative Assessment

End-of-Year Test assesses the same standards as the Beginning-of-Year Test. It is the final benchmark test for the grade level. When students' performance on the End-of-Year Test is compared to performance on the Beginning-of-Year Test, teachers are able to document students' growth.

Performance Assessment Tasks are provided for each Benchmark Test and as a Year-End Performance Assessment. Each assessment contains several tasks to assess students' ability to use what they have learned and provides an opportunity for students to display their thinking strategies. Each set of tasks is accompanied by teacher support pages and a rubric for scoring.

Performance Assessment

Performance Assessment, together with other types of assessment, can supply the missing information not provided by other testing formats. Performance Assessments, in particular, help reveal the thinking strategies students use to work through a problem. Performance Assessments with multiple tasks for each Benchmark Test and a Year-End Performance Assessment are provided in the *Getting Ready for High-Stakes Assessments*.

Each of these assessments has several tasks that target specific math concepts, skills, and strategies. These tasks can help assess students' ability to use what they have learned to solve everyday problems. Each assessment focuses on a theme. Teachers can plan for students to complete one task at a time or use an extended amount of time to complete the entire assessment.

Teacher support pages introduce each Performance Assessment. These are followed by the tasks for the students. A task-specific rubric helps teachers evaluate students' work.

Resources

Intervention Resources

For skills that students have not yet mastered, the Intervention Resources provide prescriptive information for additional instruction and practice on concepts and skills. Intervention Resources are correlated for each Common Core Standard.

Using Student and Class Record Forms

The *Getting Ready for High-Stakes Assessments* includes Student and Class Record Forms. On the Student Record Form, each test item is correlated to the standard it assesses. These forms can be used to:

- Follow progress throughout the year.
- Identify strengths, weaknesses, and provide follow-up instruction.
- Make assignments based on the intervention options provided.

High-Stakes Assessment Item Formats

The various high-stakes assessments contain item types beyond the traditional multiple-choice format, which allows for a more robust assessment of students' understanding of concepts.

Most high-stakes assessments will be administered via computers; and *Getting Ready for High-Stakes Assessments* presents items in formats similar to what students will see on the tests. The following information is provided to help teachers familiarize students with these different types of items. Each item type is identified on pages (ix–x). You may want to use the examples to introduce the item types to students.

The following explanations are provided to guide students in answering the questions. These pages (vii–viii) describe the most common item types. You may find other types on some tests.

Example 1 Identify examples of a property.

More Than One Correct Choice

This type of item may confuse students because it looks like a traditional multiple-choice item. Tell students this type of item will ask them to mark all that apply. Younger students may not understand what "mark all that apply" means. Tell them to carefully look at each choice and mark it if it is a correct answer.

Example 2 Circle the word that completes the sentence.

Choose From a List

Sometimes when students take a test on a computer, they will have to select a word, number, or symbol from a drop-down list. The *Getting Ready for High-Stakes Assessments* tests show a list and ask students to choose the correct answer. Tell students to make their choice by circling the correct answer. There will only be one choice that is correct.

Example 3 Sort numbers by categories for multiples.

Sorting

Students may be asked to sort something into categories. These items will present numbers, words, or equations on rectangular "tiles." The directions will ask students to write each of the items in the box that describes it.

When the sorting involves more complex equations or drawings, each tile will have a letter next to it. Students will be asked to write the letter for the tile in the box. Tell students that sometimes they may write the same number or word in more than one box. For example, if they need to sort quadrilaterals by category, a square could be in a box labeled rectangle and another box labeled rhombus.

Example 4 Order numbers from least to greatest.

Use Given Numbers in the Answer

Students may also see numbers and symbols on tiles when they are asked to write an equation or answer a question using only numbers. They should use the given numbers to write the answer to the problem. Sometimes there will be extra numbers. They may also need to use each number more than once.

Example 5 Match related facts.

Matching

Some items will ask students to match equivalent values or other related items. The directions will specify what they should match. There will be dots to guide them in drawing lines. The matching may be between columns or rows.

Item Types:

Example 1

More Than One Correct Choice

Fill in the bubble next to all the correct answers.

Select the equations that show the Commutative Property of Multiplication. Mark all that apply.

Ⓐ $35 \times 56 = (30 + 5) + (50 + 6)$

● B $47 \times 68 = 68 \times 47$

● C $32 \times 54 = 54 \times 32$

● D $12 \times 90 = 90 \times 12$

Ⓔ $34 \times 932 = 34 \times (900 + 30 + 2)$

Ⓕ $45 \times 167 = (40 + 5) \times 167$

Example 2

Choose From a List

Circle the word that completes the sentence.

$(25 \times 17) \times 23 = 25 \times (17 \times 23)$

The equation shows the addends in a different

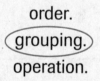

order.
(grouping.)
operation.

Example 3

Sorting

Copy the numbers in the correct box.

Write each number in the box below the heading that describes it.

30 42 72 85

Multiple of 5	Multiple of 6
30 85	30 42 72

Example 4

Use Given Numbers in the Answer

Write the given numbers to answer the question.

Write the numbers in order from least to greatest.

18,345 17,467 18,714 16,235

16,235 17,467 18,345 18,714

Example 5

Matching

Draw lines to match an item in one column to the related item in the other column.

Match the pairs of related facts.

$8 \times 7 = 56$	$8 \times 9 = 72$
$8 \times 6 = 48$	$7 \times 8 = 56$
$72 \div 9 = 8$	$9 \times 7 = 63$
$63 \div 7 = 9$	$48 \div 6 = 8$

5.OA.A.1 *Write and interpret numerical expressions.*

Name ______________________

1. Find the property that each equation shows.
Write the equation in the correct box.

15 × (7 × 9) = (15 × 7) × 9	23 + 4 + 109 = 4 + 23 + 109
13 + (3 + 7) = (13 + 3) + 7	87 × 3 = 3 × 87
1 × 9 = 9	0 + 16 = 16

Identity Property of Addition	Commutative Property of Multiplication	Identity Property of Multiplication
0 + 16 = 16	87 × 3 = 3 × 87	1 × 9 = 9
Associative Property of Multiplication	**Commutative Property of Addition**	**Associative Property of Addition**
15 × (7 × 9) = (15 × 7) × 9	23 + 4 + 109 = 4 + 23 + 109	13 + (3 + 7) = (13 + 3) + 7

2. For numbers 2a–2b, select the correct value for the expression.

2a. 55 − (12 + 2), value: 39 / (41) / 43

2b. 25 + (14 − 4) ÷ 5, value: 7 / (27) / 37

3. Carmine buys 8 plates for $1 each. He also buys 4 bowls. Each bowl costs twice as much as each plate. The store is having a sale that gives Carmine $3 off the bowls. Which numerical expression shows how much he spent?

- Ⓐ 8 + [(4 × 16) − 3]
- Ⓑ 8 + [4 × (16 + 3)]
- ● 8 + [(4 × 2) − 3]
- Ⓓ 8 + [(4 × 2) + 3]

GO ON

Name ______________________

4. Valerie earns $24 per hour. Which expression can be used to show how much money she earns in 7 hours?

- Ⓐ (7 + 20) + (7 + 4)
- ● (7 × 20) + (7 × 4)
- Ⓒ (7 + 20) × (7 + 4)
- Ⓓ (7 × 20) × (7 × 4)

5. Evaluate the numerical expression.

2 + (65 + 7) × 3 = 218

6. Jackie followed these steps to evaluate the expression 15 − (37 + 8) ÷ 3.

37 + 8 = 45

45 − 15 = 30

30 ÷ 3 = 10

Mark looks at Jackie's work and says she made a mistake.
He says she should have divided by 3 before she subtracted.

Part A

Which student is correct? Explain how you know.

Mark; Possible answer: According to the order of operations, you should perform division before subtraction.

Part B

Evaluate the expression.

37 + 8 = 45   45 ÷ 3 = 15   15 − 15 = 0

STOP

Name ____________________

1. An adult elephant eats about 300 pounds of food each day. Write an expression to represent the number of pounds of food a herd of 12 elephants eats in 5 days.

$5 \times (300 \times 12)$

2. Tara bought 2 bottles of juice a day for 15 days. On the 16th day, Tara bought 7 bottles of juice. Write an expression that matches the words.

$(2 \times 15) + 7$

3. Paul displays his sports trophies on shelves in his room. He has 5 trophies on each of 3 shelves and 2 trophies on another shelf. Write an expression to represent the number of trophies Paul displays.

$(5 \times 3) + 2$

4. Peter ran 3 miles a day for 17 days. On the 18th day, Peter ran 5 miles. Write an expression that matches the words.

$(3 \times 17) + 5$

GO ON

Name ____________________

5. Daniel bought 30 tokens when he arrived at the festival. He won 8 more tokens for getting the highest score at the basketball contest, but lost 6 tokens at the ring toss game. Write an expression to find the number of tokens Daniel has left.

$30 + 8 - 6$

6. Write $12.9 + 8$ using words.

Possible answer: Add 8 to 12 and 9 tenths.

7. Write $8 \div (7 - 5)$ using words.

Possible answer: 8 divided by the difference of 7 and 5

8. Which expressions represent multiplying the sum of 8 and 2 by 6? Mark all that apply.

Ⓐ $8 + 2 \times 6$
B $(8 + 2) \times 6$
Ⓒ $8 + (2 \times 6)$
D $6 \times (8 + 2)$
Ⓔ $6 \times 8 + 2$

STOP

Name ______________________

Practice Test
5.OA.B.3
Analyze patterns and relationships.

1. The table shows two sequences of numbers.

Day	1	2	3	4	5
Number of T-shirts sold	5	10	15	20	25
Amount earned ($)	20	40	60	80	?

For numbers 1a–1b, choose the correct values to describe how one sequence is related to the other.

1a. The unknown number in Day 5 is [90 / (100) / 120].

1b. The rule that describes how the number of T-shirts sold relates to the amount earned is [add 15 / multiply by 5 / (multiply by 4)].

2. Jawan made a table to figure out how much he earns at his job.

Job Earnings						
Week	1	2	3	4	...	6
Hours Worked	6	12	18	24	...	36
Amount Earned ($)	54	108	162	216	...	?

Part A

Write a rule that relates the amount Jawan earns to the number of hours worked. Explain how you can check your rule.

Possible answer: The rule is multiply by 9. I can check by multiplying the number of hours worked each day by 9. The product will equal the amount earned in the table.

Part B

How much does he earn from his job by the end of Week 6?

$ 324

GO ON

Name ______________________

Practice Test

3. Look for a pattern.

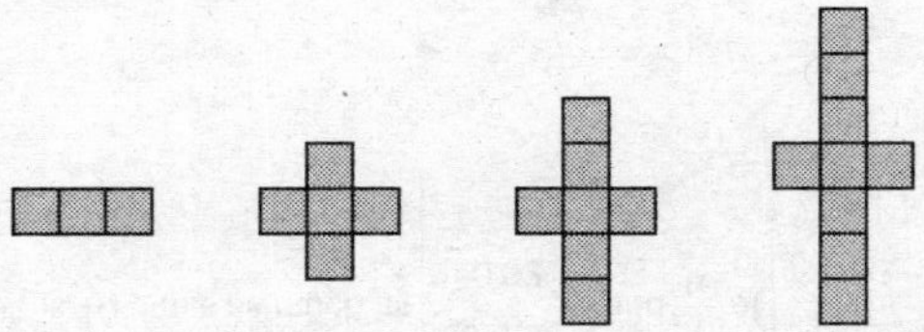

Figure 1 Figure 2 Figure 3 Figure 4

What is the rule? add 2

How many squares will there be in Figure 5? 11 squares

4. Steven is buying a new mountain bike on layaway for $272. If he pays $34 each week, how many weeks will it take Steven to pay for the bike? How can making a table help you solve the problem?

8 weeks; Possible explanation: I can make a table that shows how much Steven pays each week and the totals until I reach $272.

5. Look for a pattern.

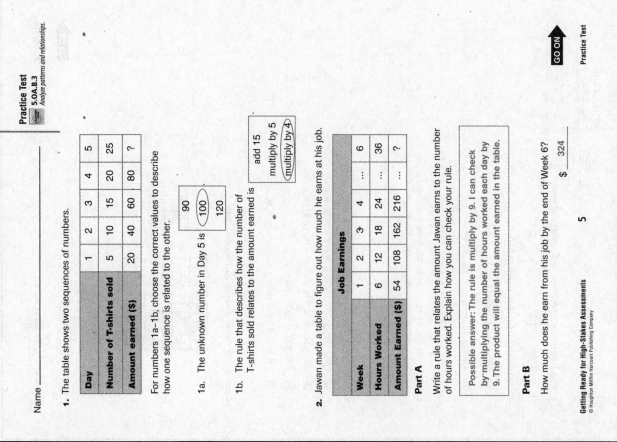

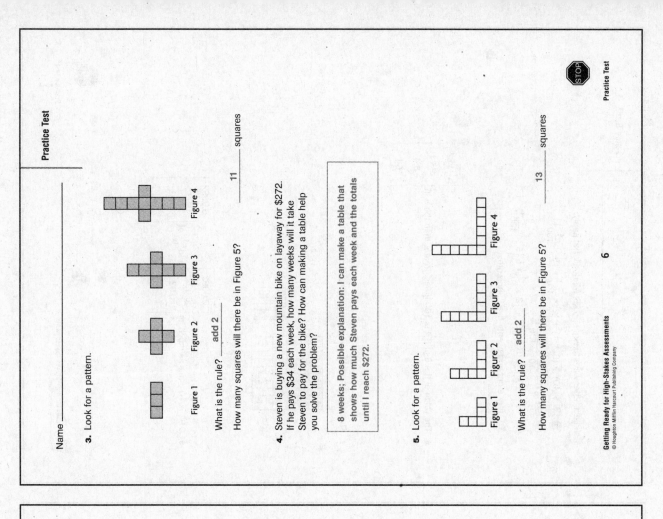

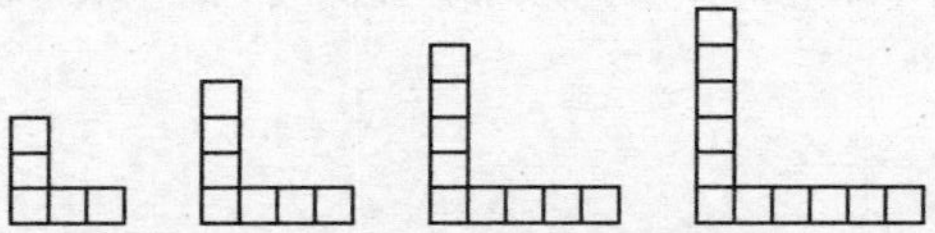

Figure 1 Figure 2 Figure 3 Figure 4

What is the rule? add 2

How many squares will there be in Figure 5? 13 squares

STOP

Name ____________

Practice Test

5.NBT.A.1 *Understand the place value system.*

1. Which statements are correct? Mark all that apply.

   (A) 170 is $\frac{1}{10}$ of 17

   (B) 660 is 10 times as much as 600

   (C) 900 is $\frac{1}{10}$ of 9,000

   (D) 4,400 is 10 times as much as 440

2. Carrie has 140 coins. She has 10 times as many coins as she had last month. How many coins did Carrie have last month?

   14

3. Select other ways to write 700,562. Mark all that apply.

   (A) $(7 \times 100{,}000) + (5 \times 1{,}000) + (6 \times 10) + (2 \times 1)$

   (B) seven hundred thousand, five hundred sixty-two

   (C) $700{,}000 + 500 + 60 + 2$

   (D) 7 hundred thousands + 5 hundreds + 62 tens

4. Shade the model to show the decimal 0.545.

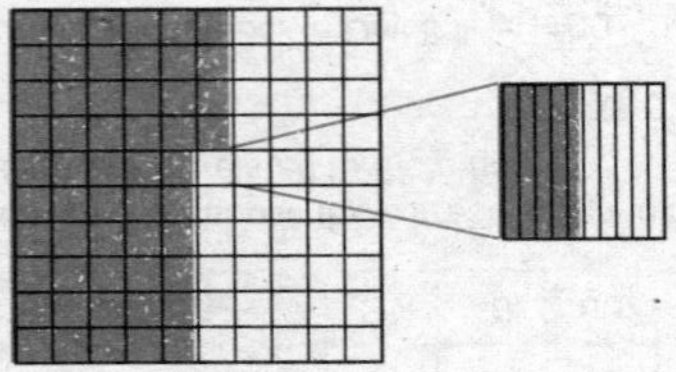

GO ON

Name ____________

Practice Test

5. Select other ways to write 58.25. Mark all that apply.

   (A) $(5 \times 10) + (8 \times 1) + \left(2 \times \frac{1}{10}\right) + \left(5 \times \frac{1}{100}\right)$

   (B) $50 + 8 + \frac{2}{10} + \frac{5}{100}$

   (C) $(5 \times 100) + (8 \times 10) + \left(2 \times \frac{1}{10}\right) + \left(5 \times \frac{1}{100}\right)$

   (D) fifty-eight and twenty-five hundredths

6. The value of the 8 in 8.4 is 100 times greater than the 8 in [**0.084** / 0.84 / 8.4 / 84]

7. Shade the model to show the decimal 0.674.

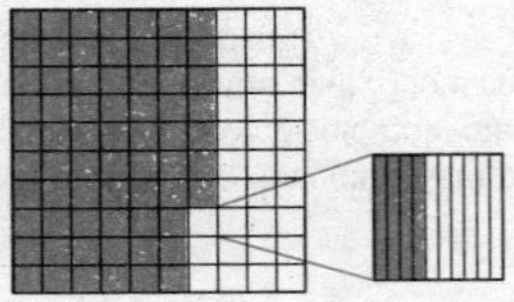

8. 0.92 is 10 times as much as [0.0092 / **0.092** / 0.92 / 9.2] and $\frac{1}{10}$ of [0.0092 / 0.092 / 0.92 / **9.2**]

STOP

Name ______________________

Practice Test
5.NBT.A.2
Understand the place value system.

1. The table shows the equations Ms. Valez discussed in math class today.

Equations
$6 \times 10^0 = 6$
$6 \times 10^1 = 60$
$6 \times 10^2 = 600$
$6 \times 10^3 = 6{,}000$

Explain the pattern of zeros in the product when multiplying by powers of 10.

Possible explanation: For each power of ten, the number of zeros written after the base is the same as the number in the exponent.

2. Omar is making a scale model of the Statue of Liberty for a report on New York City. The Statue of Liberty is 305 feet tall measuring from the ground to the tip of the torch. If the model is $\frac{1}{100}$ the actual size of the Statue of Liberty, how tall is the model?

3.05 feet

3. Which equation shows a correct product?

- (A) $0.62 \times 10 = 62$
- (B) $0.53 \times 10 = 53$
- (C) $0.09 \times 100 = 9$ (marked)
- (D) $0.60 \times 1{,}000 = 60$

GO ON

Name ______________________

Practice Test

4. Nicole is making 1,000 bows for people who donate to the library book sale. She needs a piece of ribbon that is 0.75 meter long for each bow. How many meters of ribbon does Nicole need to make the bows? Explain how to find the answer.

750 meters; Possible explanation: Multiply 1,000 by 0.75 by moving the decimal point 3 places to the right.

5. Rita is hiking along a trail that is 13.7 miles long. So far she has hiked along one-tenth of the trail. How far has Rita hiked?

1.37 miles

6. Use the numbers on the tiles to write the value of each expression. You can use a tile more than once or not at all.

$35.5 \div 10^0$	=	35.5
$35.5 \div 10$	=	3.55
$35.5 \div 10^2$	=	0.355

Tiles: . 0 3 5

7. Select other ways to express 10^4. Mark all that apply.

- (A) 10×4
- (B) $10 + 4$
- (C) 1,000
- (D) 10,000 (marked)
- (E) $10 + 10 + 10 + 10$
- (F) $10 \times 10 \times 10 \times 10$ (marked)

STOP

Name ______________________

Practice Test
5.NBT.A.3a
Understand the place value system.

1. What is the value of the underlined digit? Mark all that apply.

0.<u>6</u>79

(A) 0.6
(B) 0.06
(C) six tenths
(D) six hundredths
(E) $6 \times \frac{1}{10}$

2. Choose the value that makes the statement true.

In the number 1.025, the value of the digit 2 is 2 [ones / tenths / **hundredths** / thousandths], and the value of the digit 5 is 5 [ones / tenths / hundredths / **thousandths**].

3. What is the value of the underlined digit? Mark all that apply.

0.5<u>8</u>9

(A) 0.8
(B) 0.08
(C) eight tenths
(D) eight hundredths
(E) $8 \times \frac{1}{10}$

4. What is the value of the underlined digit? Mark all that apply.

0.2<u>8</u>3

(A) 0.8
(B) 0.08
(C) $8 \times \frac{1}{10}$
(D) $8 \times \frac{1}{100}$
(E) eight hundredths

GO ON

Name ______________________

Practice Test

5. Choose the value that makes the statement true.

In the number 2.175, the value of the digit 2 is 2 [**ones** / tenths / hundredths / thousandths], and the value of the digit 7 is 7 [ones / tenths / **hundredths** / thousandths].

6. Write 9.57 in word form.

nine and fifty-seven hundredths

7. Jon is not sure how to write 81.402 in expanded form using powers of ten. Copy and complete the expanded form of the number.

$(8 \times \boxed{10}) + (1 \times 1) + \left(4 \times \boxed{\frac{1}{10}}\right) + \left(2 \times \boxed{\frac{1}{1,000}}\right)$

8. Write $(2 \times 100) + (9 \times 1) + \left(7 \times \frac{1}{10}\right) + \left(8 \times \frac{1}{1,000}\right)$ in standard form.

209.708

STOP

Name ______________________

Practice Test
5.NBT.A.3b *Understand the place value system.*

1. Chaz kept a record of how many gallons of gas he purchased each day last week.

Day	Gas (in gallons)
Monday	4.5
Tuesday	3.9
Wednesday	4.258
Thursday	3.75
Friday	4.256

Order the days from least amount of gas Chaz purchased to greatest amount of gas Chaz purchased.

Thursday | Tuesday | Friday | Wednesday | Monday

Least → Greatest

2. For numbers 2a–2c, choose the symbol that makes the comparison true.

2a. sixteen hundredths [(>) / < / =] 0.020

2b. $3 \times \frac{1}{10} + 4 \times \frac{1}{100} + 8 \times \frac{1}{1,000}$ [> / (<) / =] one and two tenths

2c. 3.067 [> / (<) / =] $3 \times 1 + 6 \times \frac{1}{10} + 4 \times \frac{1}{1,000}$

GO ON

Name ______________________

Practice Test

3. Jasmine kept a record of how many miles she ran each week during one month.

Week	Distance (in miles)
Week 1	4.754
Week 2	4.752
Week 3	5.19
Week 4	5.75

Order the weeks from the fewest number of miles Jasmine ran to the greatest number of miles Jasmine ran.

Week 2 | Week 1 | Week 3 | Week 4

Least → Greatest

4. The four highest scores at a diving meet were 9.08, 9.1, 9.15, and 9.06 points. Choose the numbers that make the statement true.

The lowest of these four scores was [9.08 / 9.1 / 9.15 / (9.06)] points.

The highest of these four scores was [9.08 / 9.1 / (9.15) / 9.06] points.

5. In which number is the value of the digit 5 greater? Write the number in the box.

3.514 | 25 | 25

STOP

Name ______________________

5.NBT.A.4 *Understand the place value system.*

1. Which statements are correct? Mark all that apply.

(A) 16.437 rounded to the nearest whole number is 16.

(B) 16.437 rounded to the nearest tenth is 16.4.

(C) 16.437 rounded to the nearest hundredth is 16.43.

2. Rafael bought 2.15 pounds of potato salad and 4.25 pounds of macaroni salad to bring to a picnic. Which statement is correct?

(A) Rounded to the nearest whole number, Rafael bought 2 pounds of potato salad.

(B) Rounded to the nearest whole number, Rafael bought 5 pounds of macaroni salad.

(C) Rounded to the nearest tenth, Rafael bought 2.1 pounds of potato salad.

(D) Rounded to the nearest tenth, Rafael bought 4.2 pounds of potato salad.

3. Michelle records the value of one Euro in U.S. dollars each day for her social studies project. The table shows the data she has recorded so far.

Day	Value of 1 Euro (in U.S. dollars)
Monday	1.448
Tuesday	1.443
Wednesday	1.452
Thursday	1.458

On which two days was the value of 1 Euro the same when rounded to the nearest hundredth of a dollar?

Monday and Wednesday

GO ON

Name ______________________

4. The price of a certain brand of cereal at the grocery store is \$0.258 per ounce. Which statements are true? Mark all that apply.

(A) Rounded to the nearest whole number, the price is \$1 per ounce.

(B) Rounded to the nearest tenth, the price is \$0.3 per ounce.

(C) Rounded to the nearest hundredth, the price is \$0.26 per ounce.

(D) Rounded to the nearest hundredth, the price is \$0.30 per ounce.

5. Which statements are true? Mark all that apply.

(A) 1.682 inches rounded to the nearest whole number is 1 inch.

(B) 1.682 inches rounded to the nearest whole number is 2 inches.

(C) 1.682 inches rounded to the nearest tenth is 1.6 inches.

(D) 1.682 inches rounded to the nearest hundredth is 1.68 inches.

6. Trudy is going to London next summer. Each week, she records the value of one British pound in U.S. dollars. The table shows the data she has recorded so far.

Week	Value of 1 British Pound (in U.S dollars)
1	1.598
2	1.616
3	1.634
4	1.623

For which two weeks was the value of 1 British pound the same when rounded to the nearest hundredth of a dollar?

Weeks 2 and 4

STOP

5.NBT.B.5 *Perform operations with multi-digit whole numbers and with decimals to hundredths.*

Name ______________________

1. It is 3,452 feet round trip to Craig's school. If he went to school 179 times this year, how many feet did he travel in all?

617,908 feet

2. Solve. Show your work

$$\begin{array}{r} 4{,}193 \\ \times\ 381 \\ \hline \end{array}$$

1,597,533; Check students' work.

3. Jeannette eats an average of 2,125 calories each day for a year. In a 365-day year, what is the total number of calories Jeanette eats?

775,625 calories

4. For numbers 4a–4c, fill in the number that completes the equation.

4a. 1,205 × 321 = 386,805

4b. 1,362 × 409 = 557,058

4c. 1,181 × 236 = 278,716

GO ON

Name ______________________

5. A large factory pays each new employee a salary of $2,880 per month. The factory is hired to make a new product and needs to hire many new employees. Which statements are true? Mark all that apply.

- Ⓐ 100 new employees will earn a total of $28,880 in a month.
- **(B)** 111 new employees will earn a total of $319,680 in a month.
- **(C)** 150 new employees will earn a total of $432,000 in a month.
- Ⓓ 175 new employees will earn a total of $650,400 in a month.

6. It is 1,325 feet from Kinsey's house to her friend Carlito's house. When she visits Carlito, she walks to his house and gets a ride home from Carlito's mom. How many feet does Kinsey walk to Carlito's house in 112 visits?

148,400 feet

7. Solve. Show your work

$$\begin{array}{r} 2{,}996 \\ \times\ 743 \\ \hline \end{array}$$

2,226,028; Check students' work.

8. A machine can seal 179 envelopes in 1 minute. If there are 1,440 minutes in a 24-hour day, how many envelopes can the machine seal in 1 day?

257,760 envelopes

STOP

Name ______________________

Practice Test

5.NBT.B.6 *Perform operations with multi-digit whole numbers and with decimals to hundredths.*

1. Jill wants to find the quotient. Use multiplication and the Distributive Property to help Jill find the quotient.

144 ÷ 8 = **18**

Multiplication: **18 × 8 = 144**

Distributive Property: **(8 × 10) + (8 × 8) = 144**

2. Choose the word that makes the sentence true.
The first digit in the quotient of 1,875 ÷ 9

will be in the [ones / tens / **(hundreds)** / thousands] place.

3. Dana is making a seating chart for an awards banquet. There are 184 people coming to the banquet. If 8 people can be seated at each table, how many tables will be needed for the awards banquet?

23 tables

4. Which equation shows a correct quotient?

- **(A) 225 ÷ 9 = 25** (filled)
- (B) 154 ÷ 8 = 22
- (C) 312 ÷ 9 = 39
- (D) 412 ÷ 2 = 260

GO ON

Name ______________________

Practice Test

5. Write the letter for each quick picture under the division problem it represents.

A
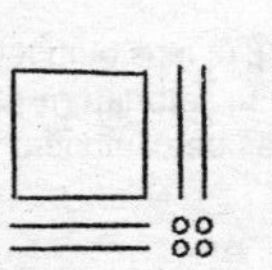

B
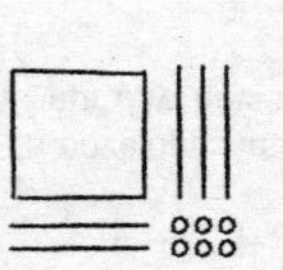

C
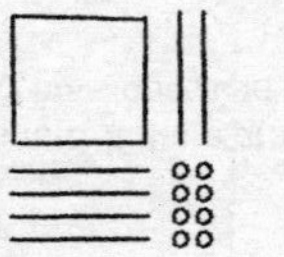

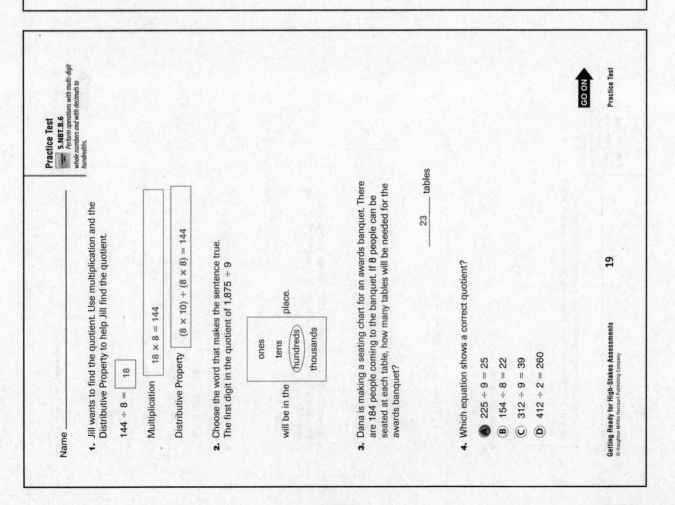

156 ÷ 12 = 13	168 ÷ 12 = 14	144 ÷ 12 = 12
B	**C**	**A**

6. Divide 575 by 14 by using partial quotients. What is the quotient? Show your work.

Possible work shown.

14)575		
− 140	10 × 14	10
435		
− 140	10 × 14	10
295		
− 140	10 × 14	10
155		
− 140	10 × 14	10
15		
− 14	1 × 14	+ 1
1		41

41 r1;

STOP

Name ______________

5.NBT.B.7 *Perform operations with multi-digit whole numbers and with decimals to hundredths.*

1. Clayton Road is 2.35 miles long. Wood Pike Road is 1.7 miles long. Kisha used a quick picture to find the combined length of Clayton Road and Wood Pike Road. Does Kisha's work make sense? Explain why or why not. Then find the correct length of the combined trails.

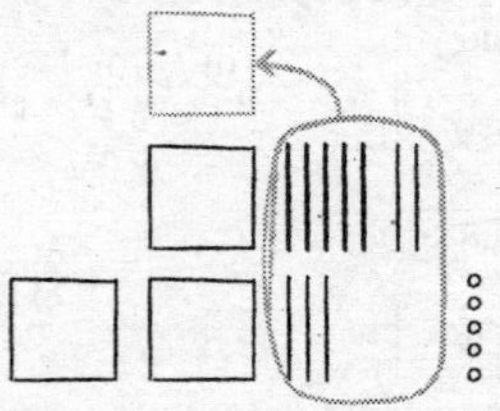

Yes. Possible explanation: She regrouped the 10 tenths as 1 one and added the 1 to the whole numbers. The combined length of the 2 trails is 4.05 miles.

2. A vet measured the mass of two birds. The mass of the robin was 76.64 grams. The mass of the blue jay was 81.54 grams. What was the difference in the masses of the birds?

4.9 grams

3. Ken and Leah are trying to solve a science homework question. They need to find out how much a rock that weighs 4 pounds on Earth would weigh on Venus. They know they can multiply the amount the rock weighs on Earth by 0.91 to find its weight on Venus. Select the partial products Ken and Leah would need to add to find the product of 4 and 0.91. Mark all that apply.

Ⓐ 0.95
● **B** 0.04
Ⓒ 3.65
● **D** 3.6
Ⓔ 0.3.6

GO ON

Name ______________

4. Write each number in a box next to the expression that has the same value. A number may be used more than once.

8.99 | 89.9 | 899

$29 \times 3.1 =$ **89.9**

$0.29 \times 31 =$ **8.99**

$2.9 \times 31 =$ **89.9**

5. Melinda, Zachary, and Heather went to the mall to shop for school supplies. Melinda spent $14.25 on her supplies. Zachary spent $2.30 more than Melinda spent. Heather spent 2 times as much money as Zachary spent. How much did Heather spend on school supplies?

$ **33.10**

6. Draw a model to show 5.5 ÷ 5.

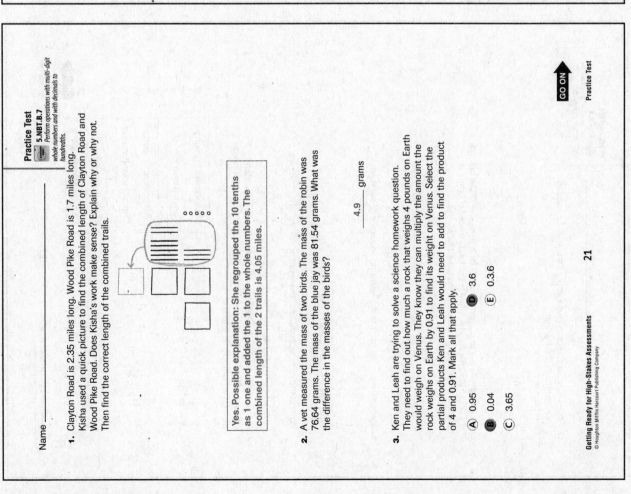

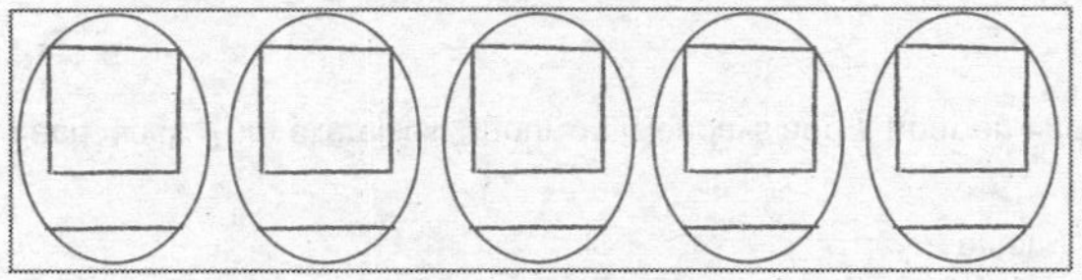

$5.5 \div 5 =$ **1.1**

7. Emma, Brandy, and Damian will cut a rope that is 29.8 feet long into 4 jump ropes. Each of the 4 jump ropes will be the same length. Write a division sentence to find the length of each rope.

29.8 ÷ 4 = 7.45

STOP

Practice Test

5.NF.A.1 *Use equivalent fractions as a strategy to add and subtract fractions.*

Name ______________________

1. Write equivalent fractions for $\frac{2}{5}$ and $\frac{1}{3}$ that could be used to find the sum of the fractions.

Possible answers:

$\boxed{\frac{6}{15}}$ and $\boxed{\frac{5}{15}}$

2. Jill brought $2\frac{1}{3}$ boxes of carrot muffins for a bake sale. Mike brought $1\frac{3}{4}$ boxes of apple muffins. What is the total number of boxes of muffins Jill and Mike brought to the bake sale?

$4\frac{1}{12}$ boxes of muffins

3. Joshua uses a rule to write the following sequence of numbers.

$\frac{1}{6}, \frac{1}{2}, \frac{5}{6},$ ______, $1\frac{1}{2}$

What rule did Joshua use? $\boxed{\text{add } \frac{1}{3}}$

What is the missing number in the sequence? $\boxed{1\frac{1}{6}}$

4. For numbers 4a–4c, tell whether each expression was rewritten using the Commutative Property or the Associative Property. Choose the correct property of addition.

4a. $\frac{1}{6} + \left(\frac{7}{8} + \frac{5}{6}\right) = \frac{1}{6} + \left(\frac{5}{6} + \frac{7}{8}\right)$ — Associative Property / **(Commutative Property)** (circled)

4b. $\left(\frac{7}{10} + \frac{1}{3}\right) + \frac{1}{10} = \left(\frac{1}{3} + \frac{7}{10}\right) + \frac{1}{10}$ — Associative Property / **(Commutative Property)** (circled)

4c. $\left(6\frac{2}{5} + \frac{4}{9}\right) + 3\frac{2}{9} = 6\frac{2}{5} + \left(\frac{4}{9} + 3\frac{2}{9}\right)$ — **(Associative Property)** (circled) / Commutative Property

GO ON

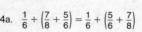

Practice Test

Name ______________________

5. Jeffrey walked $\frac{1}{3}$ mile on Monday and jogged $\frac{3}{4}$ mile on Tuesday. How far did he walk and jog on Monday and Tuesday combined? Use the tiles to complete the fraction strip model to show how you found your answer. The fractions may be used more than once or not at all.

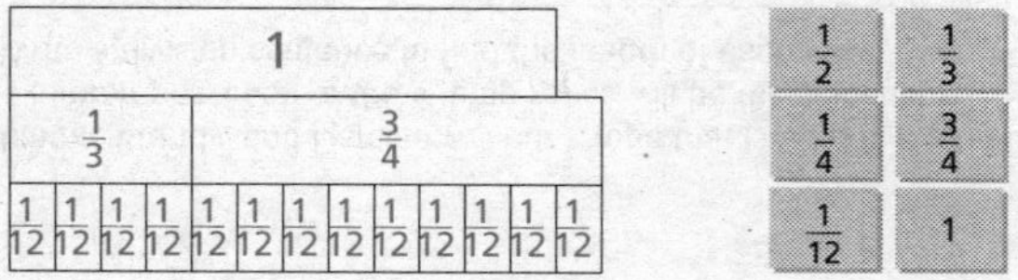

$1\frac{1}{12}$ mile(s)

6. Each week, Tom exercises $\frac{4}{5}$ hour on Mondays and $\frac{5}{6}$ hour on Fridays.

Part A

Complete the calculations below to write equivalent fractions with a common denominator. **Possible answers given.**

$\frac{4}{5} = \frac{4 \times \boxed{6}}{5 \times \boxed{6}} = \frac{\boxed{24}}{\boxed{30}}$ $\qquad$ $\frac{5}{6} = \frac{5 \times \boxed{5}}{6 \times \boxed{5}} = \frac{\boxed{25}}{\boxed{30}}$

Part B

How much time does Tom spend exercising on Monday and Friday each week? Explain how you found your answer.

$1\frac{19}{30}$ hours; Possible answer: To find the total amount of time spent exercising, I added the numerators and kept the same denominator to find $\frac{24}{30} + \frac{25}{30} = \frac{49}{30}$. Then I regrouped $\frac{30}{30}$ as 1, leaving $\frac{19}{30}$ left over. I wrote the answer as $1\frac{19}{30}$.

Part C

Last week, Tom spent $\frac{1}{10}$ hour less time than normal exercising. How much time did Tom spend exercising last week? Explain.

$1\frac{16}{30}$ hours; Possible answer: I changed $\frac{1}{10}$ to $\frac{3}{30}$. I then subtracted $\frac{3}{30}$ from the sum of the other 2 fractions. $1\frac{19}{30} - \frac{3}{30} = 1\frac{16}{30}$.

STOP

Name ______________________

Practice Test
5.NF.A.2
Use equivalent fractions as a strategy to add and subtract fractions.

1. The shaded part of the diagram shows what portion of a full meter of string Genie has. She will use $\frac{3}{5}$ meter of string to make bracelets. How much of the string will she have left after making the bracelets?

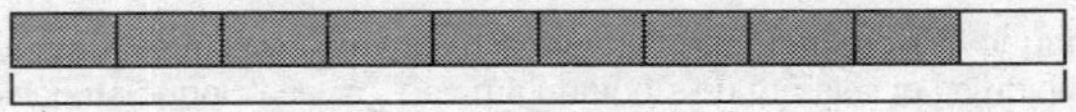

Ⓐ $\frac{1}{10}$ meter

● (B) $\frac{3}{10}$ meter

Ⓒ $\frac{3}{5}$ meter

Ⓓ $\frac{6}{5}$ meter

2. Sophia babysat for $3\frac{7}{12}$ hours on Friday. She babysat for $2\frac{5}{6}$ hours on Saturday. For numbers 2a–2c, estimate how long Sophia babysat on Friday and Saturday combined. Choose the correct benchmarks and sum.

2a. Sophia babysat for about [2 / 3 / **($3\frac{1}{2}$)** / 4] hours on Friday.

2b. Sophia babysat for about [1 / 2 / $2\frac{1}{2}$ / **(3)**] hours on Saturday.

2c. Sophia babysat for about [5 / $5\frac{1}{2}$ / 6 / **($6\frac{1}{2}$)**] hours on Friday and Saturday combined.

GO ON

Name ______________________

Practice Test

3. Four students spent time volunteering last weekend. The table shows how much time each student spent volunteering.

Volunteering	
Student	**Time (in hours)**
Amy	$4\frac{5}{6}$
Beth	$6\frac{1}{2}$
Victor	$5\frac{3}{4}$
Cal	$5\frac{2}{3}$

Match each pair of students with the difference between how much time they spent volunteering.

Amy and Victor • ——— • $\frac{3}{4}$ hour

Cal and Beth • ——— • $\frac{11}{12}$ hour

Beth and Victor • ——— • $\frac{5}{6}$ hour

(Answer: Amy and Victor — $\frac{11}{12}$ hour; Cal and Beth — $\frac{5}{6}$ hour; Beth and Victor — $\frac{3}{4}$ hour)

4. Rodrigo practiced playing the guitar $15\frac{1}{3}$ hours over the past 3 weeks. He practiced for $6\frac{1}{4}$ hours during the first week and $4\frac{2}{3}$ hours during the second week. How much time did Rodrigo spend practicing during the third week? Use the numbers and symbols to write an equation that represents the problem. Then solve the equation. Symbols may be used more than once or not at all.

$15\frac{1}{3}$ | $6\frac{1}{4}$ | $4\frac{2}{3}$ | x | = | +

Possible answer: $15\frac{1}{3} = 6\frac{1}{4} + 4\frac{2}{3} + x$

Practice time during third week: $4\frac{5}{12}$ hours

STOP

Name ____________________

Practice Test

5.NF.B.3 *Apply and extend previous understandings of multiplication and division to multiply and divide fractions.*

1. Samuel needs 233 feet of wood to build a fence. The wood comes in lengths of 11 feet.

Part A

How many total pieces of wood will Samuel need? Explain your answer.

22 pieces; Possible explanation: I need to divide 233 by 11. The answer is $21\frac{2}{11}$. Since Samuel can't buy a partial piece of wood, I need to add 1 to the quotient. So, the final answer is 22.

Part B

Theresa needs twice as many feet of wood as Samuel. How many pieces of wood does Theresa need? Explain your answer.

43 pieces of wood; Possible explanation: Twice the length of 233 feet is 466 feet. If I divide 466 by 11, the answer is $42\frac{4}{11}$. Theresa needs to buy 43 pieces of wood.

2. Twelve pounds of beans are distributed equally into 8 bags to give out at the food bank. How many pounds of beans are in each bag?

$\frac{3}{2}$ or $1\frac{1}{2}$ pounds

3. Five friends share 3 bags of trail mix equally. What fraction of a bag of trail mix does each friend get?

Each friend will receive $\frac{3}{5}$ of a bag of trail mix.

4. Zoe has 5 cucumbers she grew in her garden. She wants to share them equally among 4 of her neighbors. How many cucumbers will each neighbor receive? Use the numbers on the tiles to complete the number sentence. You may use a number more than once or not at all.

1	2	3
4	5	6

$5 \div 4 = \frac{5}{4} = 1\frac{1}{4}$

GO ON

Name ____________________

Practice Test

5. Steve is buying apples for the fifth grade. Each bag holds 12 apples. If there are 75 students total, how many bags of apples will Steve need to buy if he wants to give one apple to each student?

7 bags

6. Russ and Vickie are trying to solve this problem: There are 146 students taking buses to the museum. If each bus holds 24 students, how many buses will they need?

Russ says the students need 6 buses. Vickie says they need 7 buses. Who is correct? Explain your reasoning.

Vickie is correct. The answer to the problem is $6\frac{2}{24}$. This means that there are 6 full buses of students and 2 extra students. Those 2 students must also travel by bus to the museum; so, an extra bus is needed, making the total 7 buses.

7. Seven friends picked 7 quarts of blueberries. Three of the friends will share 4 quarts of blueberries equally, and the other 4 friends will share 3 quarts of the blueberries equally. In which group does each friend get a greater amount of blueberries? Explain your reasoning.

The group of 3 friends will get a greater amount of blueberries. Possible explanation: $4 \div 3 = \frac{4}{3}$ and $3 \div 4 = \frac{3}{4}$

$\frac{4}{3} = 1\frac{1}{3}$

$1\frac{1}{3} > \frac{3}{4}$

8. Nine friends share 3 pumpkin pies equally. What fraction of a pumpkin pie does each friend get?

Each friend will get **$\frac{3}{9}$ or $\frac{1}{3}$** of a pumpkin pie.

STOP

Name ______

Practice Test

5.NF.B.4a
Apply and extend previous understandings of multiplication and division to multiply and divide fractions.

1. Mrs. Williams is organizing her office supplies. There are 3 open boxes of paper clips in her desk drawer. Each box has $\frac{7}{8}$ of the paper clips remaining. How many boxes of paper clips are left? Shade the model and complete the calculations below to show how you found your answer.

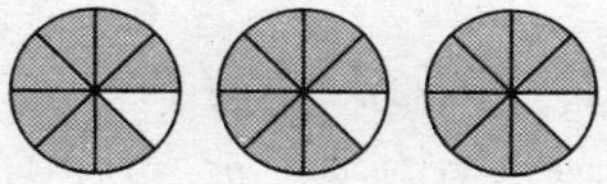

$3 \times \frac{7}{8} = \frac{21}{8} = 2\frac{5}{8}$ full boxes of paper clips

2. Logan bought 15 balloons. Four-fifths of the balloons are purple. How many of the balloons are purple? Draw a model to show how you found your answer.

Possible answer:

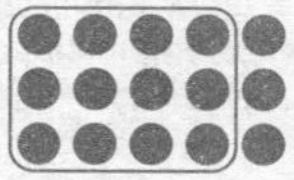

12 purple balloons

3. Taniqua took a test that had 20 multiple-choice questions and 10 True/False questions. She got $\frac{9}{10}$ of the multiple-choice questions correct, and she got $\frac{4}{5}$ of the True/False questions correct.

3a. How many multiple-choice questions did Taniqua get correct?

18 multiple-choice questions

3b. How many True/False questions did Taniqua get correct?

8 True/False questions

GO ON

Name ______

Practice Test

4. Frannie put $\frac{2}{3}$ of her music collection on an mp3 player. While on vacation, she listened to $\frac{3}{5}$ of the music on the player. How much of Frannie's music collection did she listen to while on vacation? For numbers 4a–4d, choose the correct values to describe how to solve the problem.

4a. Draw a rectangular array with 3 rows and [3 / 4 / **5** (circled)] columns.

4b. Shade [1 / **2** (circled) / 3] of the rows gray.

4c. Shade [3 / 5 / **6** (circled)] of the gray squares black.

4d. Frannie listened to [$\frac{2}{5}$ (circled) / $\frac{3}{5}$ / $\frac{3}{10}$] of her music collection while on vacation.

5. In a fifth grade class, $\frac{4}{5}$ of the girls have brown hair. Of the brown-haired girls, $\frac{3}{4}$ of them have long hair. Of the girls with long brown hair, $\frac{1}{3}$ of them have green eyes.

Part A

What fraction of the girls in the class have long brown hair?

$\frac{3}{5}$ of the girls

Part B

What fraction of the girls in the class have long brown hair and green eyes?

$\frac{1}{5}$ of the girls

STOP

5.NF.B.4b *Apply and extend previous understandings of multiplication and division to multiply and divide fractions.*

Name ______________________

1. Caleb's family room has the dimensions shown. He needs to find the area of the room so that he knows how much carpet to buy. Complete the area model below to find the area of the family room.

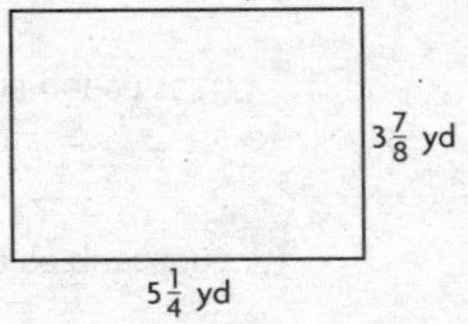

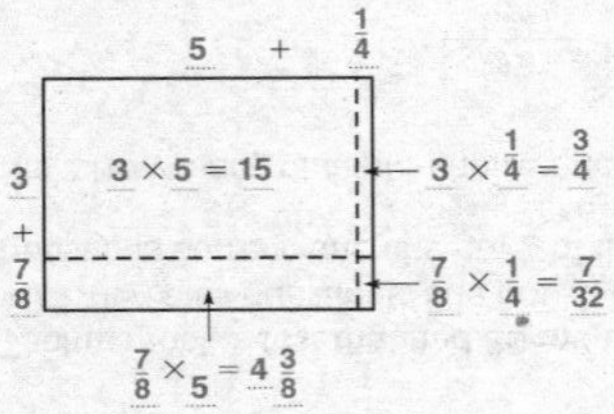

area of the room = $20\frac{11}{32}$ square yards

2. Louis wants to carpet the rectangular floor of his basement. The basement has an area of 864 square feet. The width of the basement is $\frac{2}{3}$ its length. What is the length of Louis's basement?

36 feet

3. A postcard has an area of 24 square inches. Two enlargements of the postcard have areas of 54 square inches and 96 square inches. In each postcard, the length is $1\frac{1}{2}$ times the width. Which of the following could be the dimensions of the postcard or one of the enlargements? Mark all that apply.

- (A) 6 inches by 9 inches
- (B) 10 inches by 15 inches
- (C) 8 inches by 12 inches
- (D) 6 inches by 12 inches
- (E) 4 inches by 6 inches

4. The Gilberts are designing a rectangular patio. The patio has an area of 432 square feet. The width of the patio is $\frac{3}{4}$ its length. What is the length of the patio?

24 feet

GO ON

Name ______________________

5. Peggy is making a quilt using panels that are $\frac{1}{2}$ foot by $\frac{1}{2}$ foot. The quilt is $5\frac{1}{2}$ feet long and 4 feet wide.

Part A

Let each square of the grid below represent $\frac{1}{2}$ foot by $\frac{1}{2}$ foot. Draw a rectangle on the grid to represent the quilt.

Possible answer:

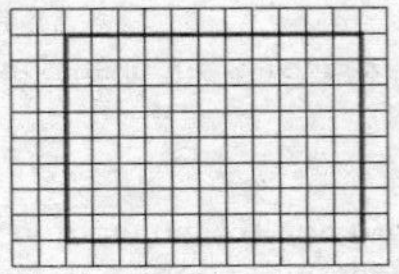

Part B

What is the area of the quilt? Explain how you found your answer.

22 square feet

Possible explanation: There are 8 rows and 11 columns of squares, for a total of $8 \times 11 = 88$ squares. Each square represents an area of $\frac{1}{2} \times \frac{1}{2} = \frac{1}{4}$ square foot. So, the area of the quilt is $88 \times \frac{1}{4} = 22$ square feet.

6. An area rug has an area of 48 square feet. Two similar rugs have areas of 108 square feet and 192 square feet. In each rug, the length is $1\frac{1}{3}$ times the width. Which of the following could be the dimensions of one of the area rugs? Mark all that apply.

- (A) 6 feet by 8 feet
- (B) 10 feet by 18 feet
- (C) 9 feet by 12 feet
- (D) 12 feet by 16 feet
- (E) 4 feet by 12 feet

STOP

Name ____________________

Practice Test

5.NF.B.5a *Apply and extend previous understandings of multiplication and division to multiply and divide fractions.*

1. Diana worked on her science project for $5\frac{1}{3}$ hours. Gabe worked on his science project $1\frac{1}{4}$ times as long as Diana. Paula worked on her science project $\frac{3}{4}$ times as long as Diana. Which statements are correct? Mark all that apply.

- (A) Diana worked longer on her science project than Gabe worked on his science project.
- ● (B) Paula worked less on her science project than Diana worked on her science project.
- ● (C) Gabe worked longer on his science project than Paula worked on her science project.
- (D) Gabe worked longer on his science project than Diana and Paula combined.

2. Write each multiplication expression in the correct box.

$\frac{4}{5} \times 1\frac{1}{8}$ $\quad \frac{1}{3} \times \frac{4}{5}$ $\quad 3 \times \frac{4}{5}$ $\quad \frac{4}{5} \times \frac{4}{5}$ $\quad \frac{8}{8} \times \frac{4}{5}$ $\quad \frac{4}{5} \times \frac{2}{2}$

Product is equal to $\frac{4}{5}$.	Product is greater than $\frac{4}{5}$.	Product is less than $\frac{4}{5}$.
$\frac{8}{8} \times \frac{4}{5}, \frac{4}{5} \times \frac{2}{2}$	$\frac{4}{5} \times 1\frac{1}{8}, 3 \times \frac{4}{5}$	$\frac{1}{3} \times \frac{4}{5}, \frac{4}{5} \times \frac{4}{5}$

3. Doreen lives $\frac{3}{4}$ mile from the library. Sheila lives $\frac{1}{3}$ as far away from the library as Doreen. Which statement is correct?

- ● (A) Doreen lives farther from the library than Sheila.
- (B) Shelia lives $\frac{1}{3}$ mile from the library.
- (C) Sheila lives twice as far from the library as Doreen.
- (D) Sheila and Doreen live the same distance from the library.

GO ON

Name ____________________

Practice Test

4. Write each multiplication expression in the correct box.

$\frac{5}{6} \times \frac{2}{3}$ $\quad 2 \times \frac{5}{6}$ $\quad \frac{5}{6} \times \frac{4}{4}$ $\quad \frac{5}{6} \times \frac{7}{3}$ $\quad \frac{10}{10} \times \frac{5}{6}$ $\quad \frac{5}{6} \times \frac{5}{6}$

Product is equal to $\frac{5}{6}$.	Product is greater than $\frac{5}{6}$.	Product is less than $\frac{5}{6}$.
$\frac{5}{6} \times \frac{4}{4}, \frac{10}{10} \times \frac{5}{6}$	$2 \times \frac{5}{6}, \frac{5}{6} \times \frac{7}{3}$	$\frac{5}{6} \times \frac{2}{3}, \frac{5}{6} \times \frac{5}{6}$

5. Stuart rode his bicycle $6\frac{3}{5}$ miles on Friday. On Saturday he rode $1\frac{1}{3}$ times as far as he rode on Friday. On Sunday he rode $\frac{5}{6}$ times as far as he rode on Friday. Which statements are correct? Mark all that apply.

- ● (A) Stuart rode more miles on Saturday than he rode on Friday.
- (B) Stuart rode more miles on Friday than he rode on Saturday and Sunday combined.
- ● (C) Stuart rode fewer miles on Sunday than he rode on Friday.
- (D) Stuart rode more miles on Sunday than he rode on Saturday.

6. Write each multiplication expression in the correct box.

$\frac{2}{3} \times \frac{2}{3}$ $\quad \frac{5}{6} \times \frac{2}{3}$ $\quad 4\frac{1}{8} \times \frac{2}{3}$ $\quad \frac{4}{4} \times \frac{2}{3}$ $\quad \frac{2}{3} \times 2$ $\quad \frac{2}{3} \times \frac{5}{5}$

Product is equal to $\frac{2}{3}$.	Product is greater than $\frac{2}{3}$.	Product is less than $\frac{2}{3}$.
$\frac{4}{4} \times \frac{2}{3}, \frac{2}{3} \times \frac{5}{5}$	$4\frac{1}{8} \times \frac{2}{3}, \frac{2}{3} \times 2$	$\frac{2}{3} \times \frac{2}{3}, \frac{5}{6} \times \frac{2}{3}$

STOP

Name ______________________

1. A scientist had $\frac{3}{5}$ liter of solution. He used $\frac{1}{6}$ of the solution for an experiment. How much solution did the scientist use for the experiment? Use the numbers on the tiles to complete the calculations. You may use numbers more than once or not at all.

$\frac{3}{5} \times \frac{1}{6} = \frac{3 \times \boxed{1}}{5 \times \boxed{6}} = \frac{\boxed{3}}{\boxed{30}} = \frac{\boxed{1}}{\boxed{10}}$

Tiles: 1, 2, 3, 4, 6, 10, 20, 30

$\frac{1}{10}$ liter

2. For numbers 2a–2d, without multiplying, use the symbols from the list on the right to indicate that the product will compare with the factor. Symbols can be used more than once.

Symbols: <, >, =

2a. $\frac{13}{4} \times \frac{5}{8} = x$ — $x < \frac{13}{4}$ — $x > \frac{5}{8}$

2b. $\frac{4}{3} \times 6 = x$ — $x > \frac{4}{3}$ — $x > 6$

2c. $\frac{2}{5} \times \frac{1}{7} = x$ — $x < \frac{2}{5}$ — $x < \frac{1}{7}$

2d. $\frac{5}{8} \times \frac{7}{7} = x$ — $x = \frac{5}{8}$ — $x < \frac{7}{7}$

3. $\frac{4}{5} \times \frac{3}{8}$ [(<) / > / =] $\frac{4}{5}$

4. $\frac{8}{6} \times \frac{2}{3}$ [(<) / > / =] $\frac{2}{3}$

GO ON

Name ______________________

5. Without multiplying, classify each product as being less than $\frac{2}{3}$, equal to $\frac{2}{3}$, or greater than $\frac{2}{3}$. Write the letter of each expression under the correct category.

A $\frac{2}{3} \times \frac{1}{5}$ **B** $\frac{2}{3} \times \frac{8}{5}$ **C** $\frac{2}{3} \times \frac{9}{9}$ **D** $\frac{2}{3} \times \frac{6}{1}$ **E** $\frac{2}{3} \times \frac{8}{9}$ **F** $\frac{2}{3} \times 2$

Less Than $\frac{2}{3}$	Equal to $\frac{2}{3}$	Greater Than $\frac{2}{3}$
A, E	C	B, D, F

6. For numbers 6a–6d, without multiplying, use the symbols from the list on the right to indicate how the product will compare with the factor. Symbols can be used more than once.

Symbols: <, >, =

6a. $\frac{3}{4} \times \frac{15}{7} = x$ — $x > \frac{3}{4}$ — $x < \frac{15}{7}$

6b. $7 \times \frac{6}{5} = x$ — $x > 7$ — $x > \frac{6}{5}$

6c. $\frac{8}{9} \times \frac{1}{5} = x$ — $x < \frac{8}{9}$ — $x < \frac{1}{5}$

6d. $\frac{8}{8} \times \frac{7}{10} = x$ — $x < \frac{8}{8}$ — $x = \frac{7}{10}$

7. $\frac{6}{13} \times \frac{3}{4}$ [(<) / > / =] $\frac{3}{4}$

8. $\frac{4}{7} \times \frac{5}{3}$ [< / (>) / =] $\frac{4}{7}$

9. $\frac{5}{9} \times \frac{3}{3}$ [< / > / (=)] $\frac{5}{9}$

STOP

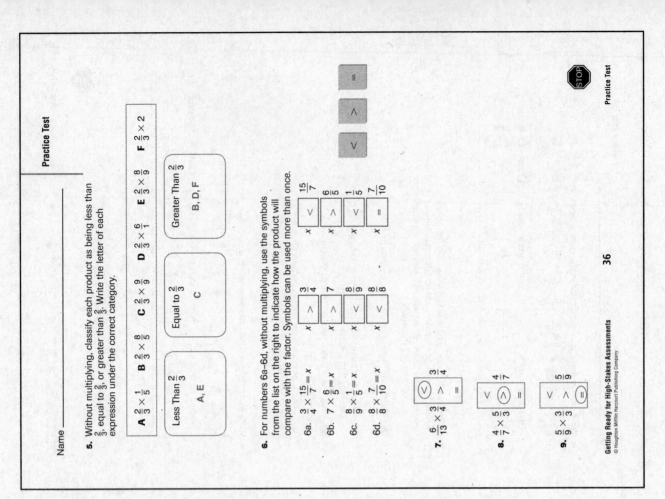

Name ________________________

Practice Test
5.NF.B.6
Apply and extend previous understandings of multiplication and division to multiply and divide fractions.

1. Kayla walks $3\frac{2}{5}$ miles each day. Which of the following statements correctly describe how far she walks? Mark all that apply.

Ⓐ Kayla walks $14\frac{2}{5}$ miles in 4 days.
● B Kayla walks $23\frac{4}{5}$ miles in 7 days.
● C Kayla walks 34 miles in 10 days.
Ⓓ Kayla walks $102\frac{2}{5}$ miles in 31 days.

2. The table shows how many hours some of the part-time employees at the toy store worked last week.

Name	Hours Worked
Conrad	$6\frac{2}{3}$
Giovanni	$9\frac{1}{2}$
Sally	$10\frac{3}{4}$

This week, Conrad will work $1\frac{3}{4}$ times longer than last week. Giovanni will work $1\frac{1}{3}$ times longer than last week. Sally will work $\frac{2}{3}$ the number of hours she worked last week. Match each employee's name to the number of hours he or she will work this week.

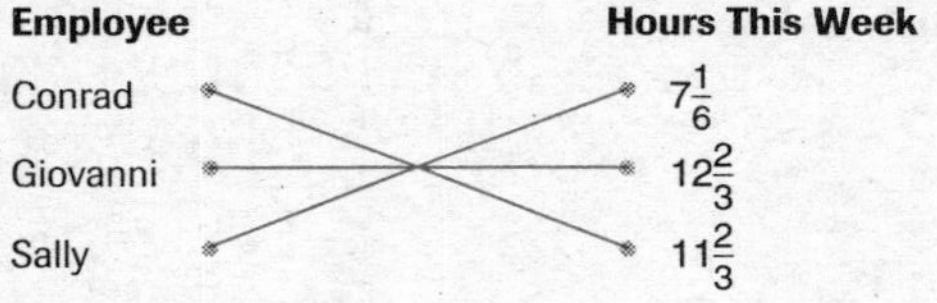

3. Jake wrote 4 equations on the board. Which of Jake's equations are correct? Mark all that apply.

Ⓐ $\frac{3}{5} \times \frac{2}{7} = \frac{21}{10}$
● B $\frac{2}{9} \times \frac{5}{3} = \frac{10}{27}$
● C $\frac{7}{8} \times \frac{5}{9} = \frac{35}{72}$
Ⓓ $\frac{1}{2} \times \frac{3}{5} = \frac{4}{10}$

GO ON

Name ________________________

Practice Test

4. Jessica is creating a banner that will be $\frac{2}{5}$ meter wide. Which statements correctly describe the area her banner will be for each length? Mark all that apply.

● A A $\frac{2}{5}$-meter-long banner will have an area of $\frac{4}{25}$ meter squared.
Ⓑ A $\frac{5}{8}$-meter-long banner will have an area of $\frac{10}{25}$ meter squared.
● C A $\frac{3}{4}$-meter-long banner will have an area of $\frac{6}{20}$ meter squared.
Ⓓ A $\frac{9}{10}$-meter-long banner will have an area of $\frac{18}{100}$ meter squared.

5. The table shows how many bags of canned goods each class collected during the first week of a food drive.

Class	Bags of Canned Goods
4th Graders	$3\frac{1}{2}$
5th Graders	$2\frac{3}{4}$
6th Graders	$3\frac{1}{4}$

Next week the 4th graders hope to collect $1\frac{1}{3}$ times as many bags of canned goods as the first week. The 5th graders' goal is to collect $1\frac{3}{4}$ times as many bags of canned goods as they collected in week 1. The 6th graders hope to collect $1\frac{1}{2}$ times as many bags of canned goods. Match each class to the number of bags of canned goods they hope to collect next week.

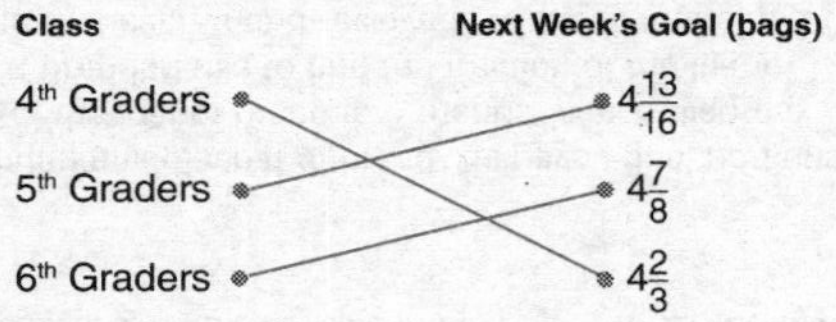

STOP

Name ____________________

1. A builder has an 8-acre plot divided into $\frac{1}{4}$-acre home sites. How many $\frac{1}{4}$-acre home sites are there?

   There are [32] home sites.

2. For numbers 2a–2e, write the number that makes the equation correct.

   2a. $3 \div \frac{1}{4} =$ [12]

   2b. [7] $\div \frac{1}{2} = 14$

   2c. $\frac{1}{5} \div 4 =$ [$\frac{1}{20}$]

   2d. [$\frac{1}{2}$] $\div 5 = \frac{1}{10}$

   2e. $\frac{1}{7} \div 3 =$ [$\frac{1}{21}$]

3. Choose the numbers to create a story problem that represents $4 \div \frac{1}{6}$.

   Bill bought [(4) / $\frac{1}{6}$ / $\frac{4}{6}$] pound(s) of cheese.

   He made grilled cheese sandwiches and used [4 / ($\frac{1}{6}$) / $\frac{4}{6}$] pound(s) of cheese in each sandwich.

   Bill made 24 sandwiches.

4. Divide. Draw a number line to show your work.

   $2 \div \frac{1}{3} =$ [6]

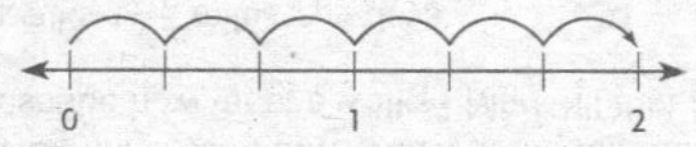

GO ON

Name ____________________

5. Adan has $\frac{1}{2}$ quart of milk. If he pours the same amount of milk into 3 glasses, each glass will contain [$\frac{1}{6}$] quart of milk.

6. Brendan made a loaf of bread. He gave equal portions of $\frac{1}{2}$ of the loaf of bread to 6 friends. Which diagram could Brendon use to find the fraction of the loaf of bread that each friend received? Mark all that apply.

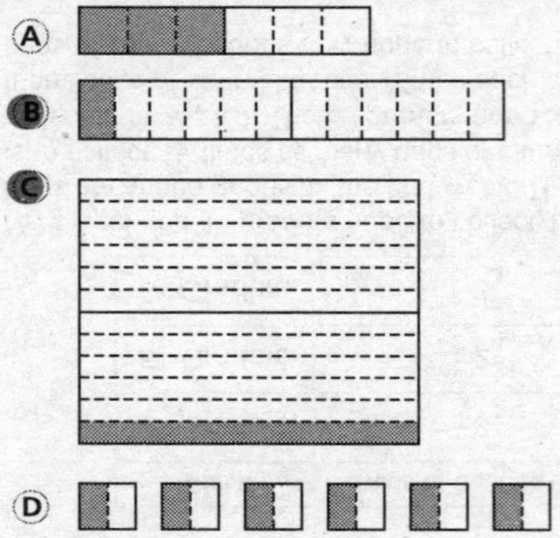

7. Landon and Colin bought $\frac{1}{2}$ pound of strawberries. They are sharing the strawberries equally. Each person will receive [$\frac{1}{4}$] pound of strawberries.

STOP

5.NF.B.7b *Apply and extend previous understandings of multiplication and division to multiply and divide fractions.*

Name ____________________

1. Gabriel made 4 small meatloaves. He cut each meatloaf into fourths. How many $\frac{1}{4}$-size pieces of meatloaf does Gabriel have? Draw lines in the model to find the answer.

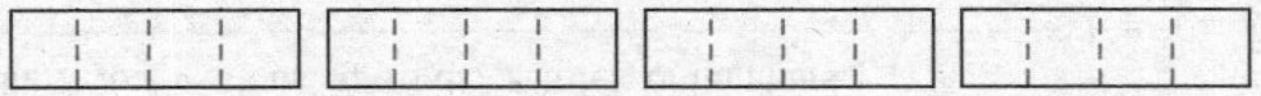

Gabriel has **16** $\frac{1}{4}$-size pieces of meatloaf.

2. Camilla has a $\frac{1}{2}$ pound of raisins that she will divide evenly into 5 bags. Shade the diagram to show the fractional part of a pound that will be in each bag.

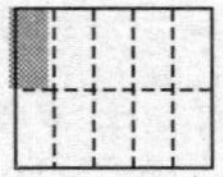

3. A 6-mile walking trail has a distance marker every $\frac{1}{3}$ mile. How many markers are along the trail?

There are **18** markers along the trail.

4. Eric has 4 pieces of clay. He cut each piece of clay into thirds. How many $\frac{1}{3}$-size pieces of clay does Eric have? Draw lines in the model to find the answer.

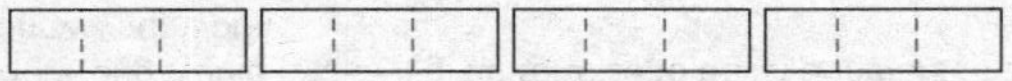

Eric has **12** $\frac{1}{3}$-size pieces of clay.

5. Cecila has $\frac{1}{3}$ pound of trail mix that she will divide equally into 3 bags. Shade the diagram to show the fractional part of a pound that will be in each bag.

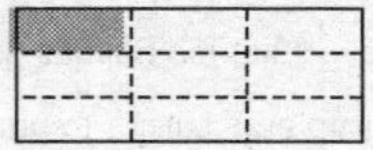

GO ON

Name ____________________

6. Adrian made 3 granola bars. He cut each bar into fourths. How many $\frac{1}{4}$-size pieces of granola bar does Adrian have? Draw lines in the model to find the answer.

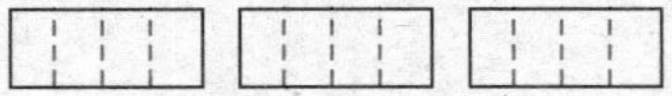

Adrian has **12** one-quarter-size pieces of granola bar.

7. Kyle made a loaf of banana bread. He gave equal portions of $\frac{1}{2}$ of the loaf to 4 friends. Which diagram could Kyle use to find the fraction of the loaf that each friend received? Mark all that apply.

Ⓐ (marked) Ⓑ Ⓒ Ⓓ (marked)

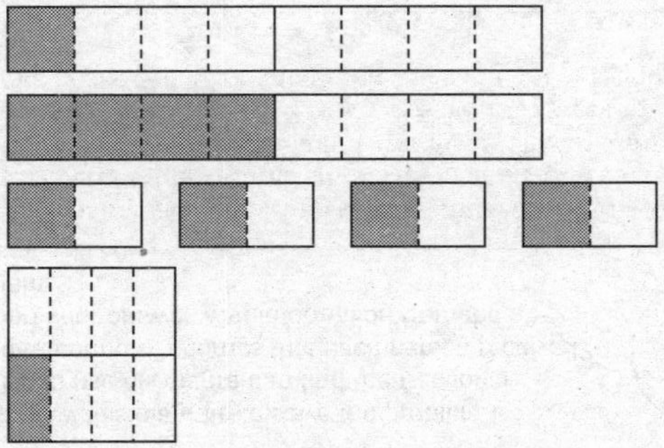

8. Ben is making bread that calls for 5 cups of flour. His measuring cup only holds $\frac{1}{2}$ cup. How many times will Ben need to fill the measuring cup to get the 5 cups of flour?

Ben will need to fill the measuring cup 10 times.

9. Tina has $\frac{1}{2}$ quart of iced tea. She pours the same amount into each of 3 glasses. Which equation represents the fraction of a quart of iced tea that is in each glass? Mark all that apply.

Ⓐ $\frac{1}{2} \div \frac{1}{3} = n$

Ⓑ $2 \div 3 = n$

Ⓒ $2 \div \frac{1}{3} = n$

Ⓓ (marked) $\frac{1}{2} \times \frac{1}{3} = n$

Ⓔ $2 \times \frac{1}{3} = n$

Ⓕ (marked) $\frac{1}{2} \div 3 = n$

STOP

Name ______________________

1. Maureen has $\frac{1}{4}$ pound of raisins. She divides the raisins into 4 servings. Each serving contains $\boxed{\frac{1}{16}}$ pound of raisins.

2. A giant tortoise can walk about $\frac{1}{10}$ meter per second on land. A cooter turtle can walk about $\frac{1}{2}$ meter per second on land.

Part A

How long would it take a giant tortoise to travel 5 meters? Show your work.

$5 \div \frac{1}{10} = 5 \times 10 = 50$

It would take the giant tortoise 50 seconds to travel 5 meters.

Part B

How much longer would it take a giant tortoise than a cooter turtle to travel 10 meters on land? Explain how you found your answer.

80 seconds longer; Possible explanation: First, I found the time it would take the giant tortoise to travel 10 meters: $10 \div \frac{1}{10} = 10 \times 10 = 100$, or 100 seconds. Then, I found the time it would take the cooter turtle to travel 10 meters: $10 \div \frac{1}{2} = 10 \times 2 = 20$, or 20 seconds. Then I subtracted $100 - 20 = 80$.

3. Dora buys one package each of 1-pound, 2-pound, and 4-pound packages of ground beef to make hamburgers.

How many $\frac{1}{4}$-pound hamburgers can she make? Show your work using words, pictures, or numbers.

Check students' work. 28 hamburgers; Possible explanation: I found the total number of pounds of ground beef Dora bought: $1 + 2 + 4 = 7$. Then, I wrote a related multiplication expression to find $7 \div \frac{1}{4}$. $7 \div \frac{1}{4} = 7 \times 4 = 28$

GO ON

Name ______________________

4. Mrs. Green wrote the following problem on the whiteboard:

Lisa and Frank shared $\frac{1}{3}$ pound of cherries equally. What fractional part of a pound did each person receive?

Part A

Molly wrote the following equation to solve the problem: $2 \div \frac{1}{3} = n$. Do you agree with Molly's equation? Support your answer with information from the problem.

No, I disagree. Possible answer: Lisa and Frank are sharing $\frac{1}{3}$ pound of cherries, and I need to divide $\frac{1}{3}$ by 2, so the correct equation is $\frac{1}{3} \div 2 = n$.

Part B

Noah drew this diagram to solve the problem. Can Noah use his diagram to find the fractional part of a pound of cherries that each person received? Support your answer with information from the problem.

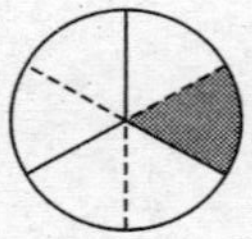

Yes. Possible answer: Noah divided the circle into 3 equal parts to represent thirds. Then, he divided each third in half. He shaded half of $\frac{1}{3}$ of the circle. So, the diagram represents $\frac{1}{3} \div 2 = \frac{1}{3} \times \frac{1}{2} = \frac{1}{6}$. Since $\frac{1}{6}$ of the circle is shaded, Lisa and Frank will each get $\frac{1}{6}$ pound of cherries.

5. Kayleigh has $\frac{1}{4}$-cup of oil. She pours the same amount into each of 2 oil lamps. Which equation represents the fraction of a cup of oil that is in each oil lamp? Mark all that apply.

- (A) $\frac{1}{2} \div \frac{1}{4} = n$
- **(B)** $\frac{1}{4} \times \frac{1}{2} = n$
- (C) $2 \div \frac{1}{4} = n$
- (D) $4 \div 2 = n$
- **(E)** $\frac{1}{4} \div 2 = n$
- (F) $2 \times \frac{1}{4} = n$

STOP

5.MD.A.1
Convert like measurement units within a given measurement system.

Name ______________________

1. The library is 5 miles from the post office. How many yards is the library from the post office?

8,800 yards

2. Billy made 3 gallons of juice for a picnic. He said that he made $\frac{3}{4}$ quart of juice. Explain Billy's mistake.

Possible explanation: Billy divided the number of gallons by 4 to convert to quarts. He should have multiplied the number of gallons by 4 to find the number of quarts in 3 gallons. $3 \times 4 = 12$ quarts

3. The Drama Club is showing a video of its recent play. The first showing begins at 2:30 P.M. The second showing is scheduled at 5:25 P.M. with a $\frac{1}{2}$-hour break between the showings.

Part A

How long is the video in hours and minutes?

2 hours and 25 minutes

Part B

Explain how you can use a number line to find the answer.

Possible explanation: I can work backward from the start time of the second showing at 5:25. I count back $\frac{1}{2}$ hour, which is 30 minutes, for the break between showings to 4:55. Then, I can find the elapsed time between 2:30 and 4:55.

Part C

The second showing started 20 minutes late. Will the second showing be over by 7:45 P.M.? Explain why your answer is reasonable.

No. Possible explanation: The second showing started at 5:45 P.M. The movie lasts 2 hours 25 minutes, so it ends at 8:10 P.M., which is later than 7:45 P.M.

GO ON

Name ______________________

4. Fred bought 4 liters of liquid laundry detergent, 3,250 milliliters of fabric softener, and 2.5 liters of bleach. Which statements are true? Mark all that apply.

- (A) Fred bought 75 milliliters more fabric softener than bleach.
- (B) Fred bought 1.75 liters more laundry detergent than bleach.
- **(C)** Fred bought 750 milliliters more fabric softener than bleach.
- (D) Fred bought 150 milliliters more laundry detergent than bleach.
- **(E)** Fred bought 0.75 liters more laundry detergent than fabric softener.

5. A male hippopotamus can weigh up to 10,000 pounds. How many tons is 10,000 pounds?

5 tons

6. Amar and his friends went to a movie at 4:45 P.M. The movie ended at 6:20 P.M.

Part A

How long was the movie?

1 hour(s) and 35 minutes

Part B

Amar got home 45 minutes after the movie ended. What time did Amar get home? Explain how you found your answer.

7:05 P.M.; Possible explanation: I need to find 45 minutes after 6:20 P.M. 6:20 to 7:00 is 40 minutes, so 5 minutes more is 7:05.

STOP

Name ____________________

Practice Test
5.MD.B.2 *Represent and interpret data.*

1. A builder is buying property to build new houses. The sizes of the lots are $\frac{1}{6}, \frac{1}{2}, \frac{1}{3}, \frac{1}{2}, \frac{1}{6}, \frac{1}{2}, \frac{1}{2}, \frac{1}{3}, \frac{1}{6}, \frac{1}{2}, \frac{1}{6}, \frac{1}{2}, \frac{1}{6}, \frac{1}{6}$, and $\frac{1}{3}$ acre. Organize the information in a line plot.

What is the average size of the lots?

$\frac{1}{3}$ acre

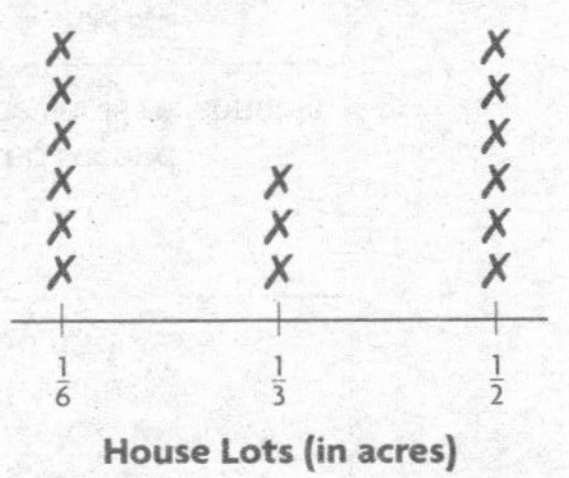

2. The line plot shows the weights of bags of beans. What is the average weight of the bags? Show your work.

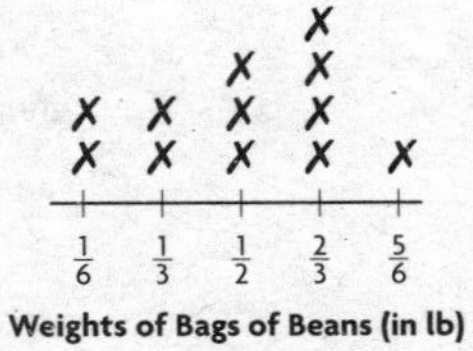

$\frac{1}{2}$ pound;

$\frac{1}{6} \times 2 = \frac{2}{6}$ or $\frac{1}{3}$; $\frac{1}{3} \times 2 = \frac{2}{3}$; $\frac{1}{2} \times 3 = \frac{3}{2}$ or $1\frac{1}{2}$

$\frac{2}{3} \times 4 = \frac{8}{3}$ or $2\frac{2}{3}$; $\frac{5}{6}$

$\frac{1}{3} + \frac{2}{3} + 1\frac{1}{2} + 2\frac{2}{3} + \frac{5}{6} = 6$

$6 \div 12 = \frac{1}{2}$

3. Amy filled bags with mixed nuts. The weights of the bags are $\frac{1}{8}$-lb, $\frac{1}{4}$-lb, $\frac{1}{8}$-lb, $\frac{1}{2}$-lb, $\frac{1}{8}$-lb, $\frac{1}{4}$-lb, $\frac{1}{8}$-lb, $\frac{1}{2}$-lb, $\frac{1}{8}$-lb, $\frac{1}{4}$-lb, $\frac{1}{8}$-lb, $\frac{1}{2}$-lb, $\frac{1}{8}$-lb, $\frac{1}{8}$-lb, $\frac{1}{4}$-lb, and $\frac{1}{2}$-lb. Organize the information in a line plot.

What is the average weight of the bags?

$\frac{1}{4}$ pound(s)

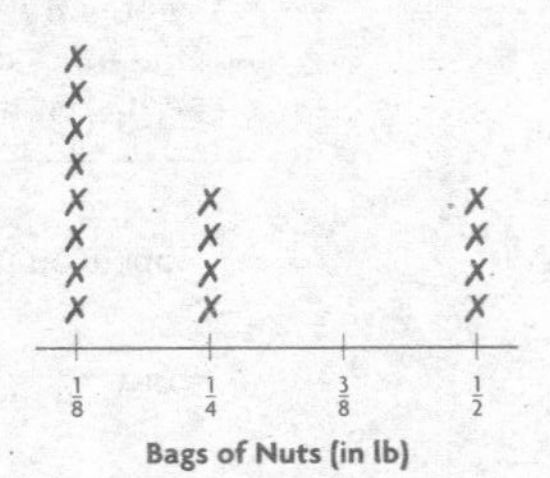

GO ON

Name ____________________

Practice Test

4. The line plot shows the weights of stones found in a stream. What is the average weight of the stones? Show your work.

$\frac{5}{11}$ pound;

$\frac{1}{6} \times 2 = \frac{2}{6}$ or $\frac{1}{3}$; $\frac{1}{3} \times 4 = \frac{4}{3}$ or $1\frac{1}{3}$; $\frac{1}{2}$; $\frac{2}{3} \times 3 = \frac{6}{3}$ or 2; $\frac{5}{6}$

$\frac{1}{3} + 1\frac{1}{3} + \frac{1}{2} + 2 + \frac{5}{6} = 5$

$5 \div 11 = \frac{5}{11}$

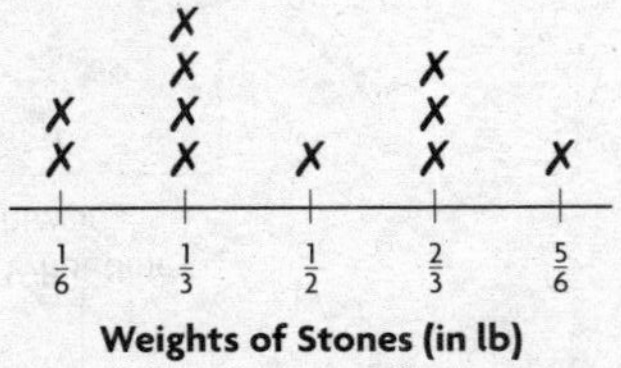

5. Mika records the number of miles she walks each day.

Part A

Graph Mika's results on the line plot.

Distance (miles)	Days
$1\frac{1}{2}$	𝍸
$1\frac{5}{8}$	|
$1\frac{3}{4}$	||
2	|
$2\frac{1}{8}$	|||
$2\frac{1}{4}$	||||

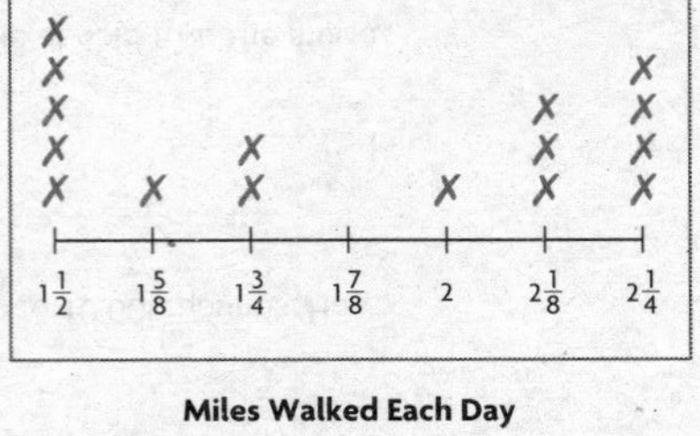

Part B

How many days did she walk and what was her total distance? Explain your thinking.

16 days for a total of 30 miles; Possible explanation: I multiplied each distance by the number of dots above the distance in the line plot, and then I added the products.

STOP

Name ____________________

Practice Test

5.MD.C.3a
Geometric measurement: understand concepts of volume and relate volume to multiplication and to addition.

1. Match the figure with the number of unit cubes that would be needed to build each figure. Not every number of unit cubes will be used.

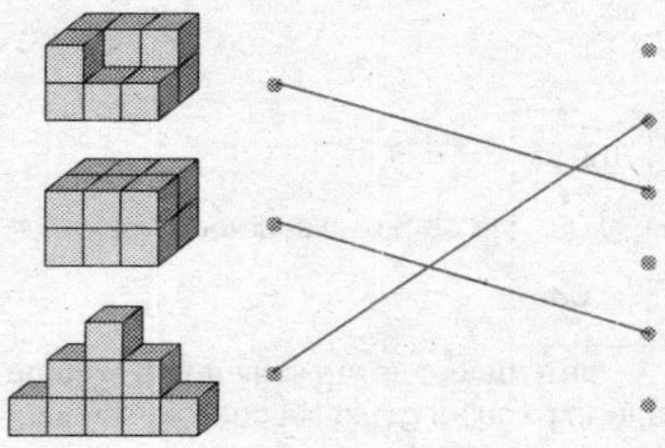

- 8 unit cubes
- 9 unit cubes
- 10 unit cubes
- 11 unit cubes
- 12 unit cubes
- 16 unit cubes

2. Match the figure with the number of unit cubes that would be needed to build each figure. Not every number of unit cubes will be used.

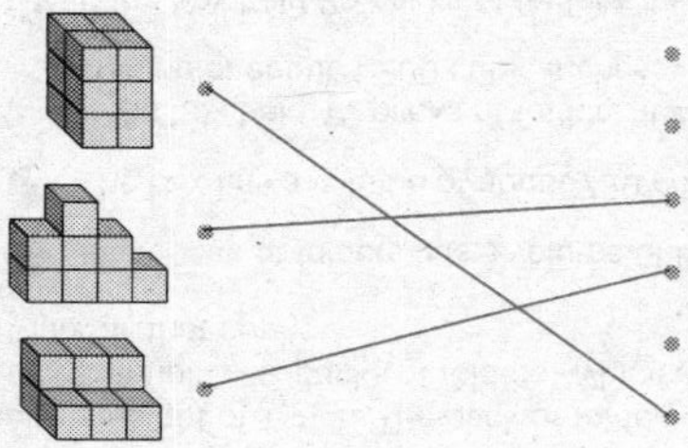

- 6 unit cubes
- 7 unit cubes
- 8 unit cubes
- 9 unit cubes
- 10 unit cubes
- 12 unit cubes

3. Bakari builds a rectangular prism using unit cubes.

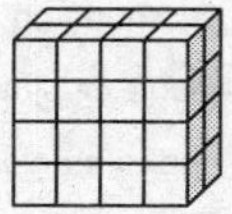

What is the volume of the prism? Explain your thinking.

32 cubic units; Possible explanation: There are 8 unit cubes on the bottom layer. Since there are 4 layers that each have 8 unit cubes, I multiplied 4 by 8 to get 32.

GO ON

Name ____________________

Practice Test

4. Match the figure with the number of unit cubes that would be needed to build each figure. Not every number of unit cubes will be used.

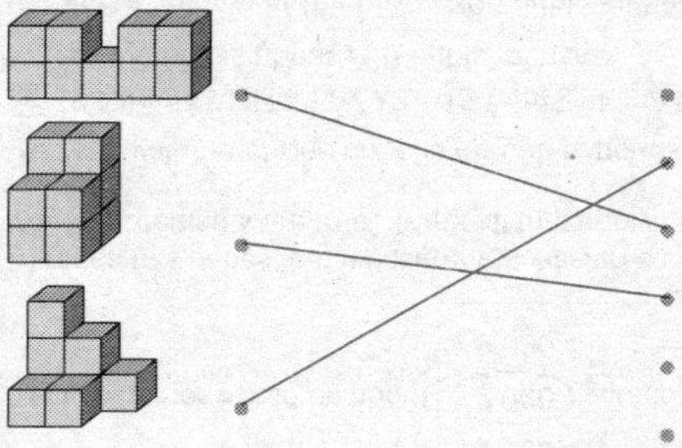

- 7 unit cubes
- 8 unit cubes
- 9 unit cubes
- 10 unit cubes
- 12 unit cubes
- 15 unit cubes

5. Joo-Chan builds a rectangular prism using unit cubes.

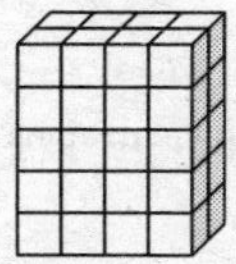

What is the volume of the prism? Explain your thinking.

40 cubic units; Possible explanation: There are 8 unit cubes on the bottom layer. Since there are 5 layers each with 8 unit cubes, I multiplied 5 by 8 to get 40.

6. Match the figure with the number of unit cubes that would be needed to build each figure. Not every number of unit cubes will be used.

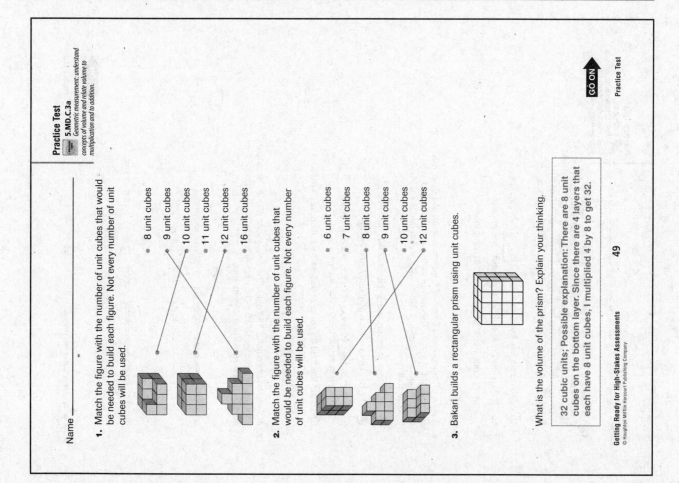

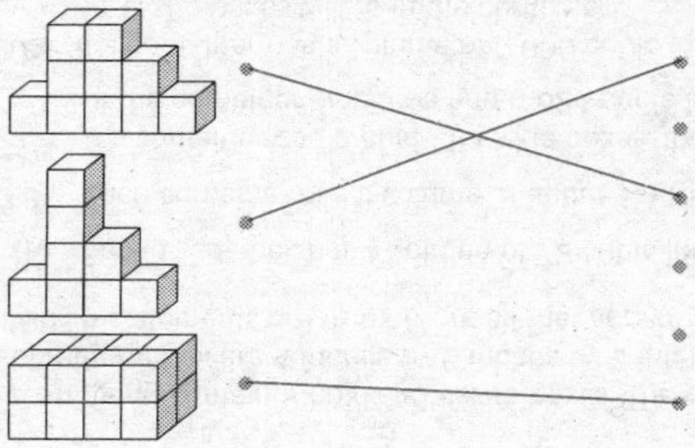

- 8 unit cubes
- 9 unit cubes
- 10 unit cubes
- 11 unit cubes
- 12 unit cubes
- 16 unit cubes

STOP

Name ________________

Practice Test

5.MD.C.3b *Geometric measurement: understand concepts of volume and relate volume to multiplication and to addition.*

1. A shipping crate holds 20 shoeboxes. The dimensions of a shoebox are 6 inches by 4 inches by 12 inches. For numbers 1a–1c, write the number that makes the sentence true.

1a. Each shoebox has a volume of [288] cubic inches.

1b. Each crate has a volume of about [5,760] cubic inches.

1c. If the crate could hold 27 shoeboxes, the volume of the crate would be about [7,776] cubic inches.

2. A pack of folders has a length of 5 inches, a width of 12 inches, and a height of 1 inch. The pack of folders will be shipped in a box that holds 12 packs of folders. Which statements are true? Mark all that apply.

- (A) ● Each pack of folders has a volume of 60 cubic inches.
- (B) ● The box has a volume of about 720 cubic inches.
- (C) If the box held 15 packs of folders, it would have a volume of about 1,200 cubic inches.
- (D) ● If the box held 20 packs of folders, it would have a volume of about 1,200 cubic inches.

3. A shipping crate holds 18 books. The dimensions of each book are 2 inches by 8 inches by 10 inches. For numbers 3a–3b, choose the number that makes the statement true.

3a. Each book has a volume of [20 / 80 / (160)] cubic inches.

3b. Each crate has a volume of about [160 / (2,880) / 3,220] cubic inches.

GO ON

Name ________________

Practice Test

4. A shipping container holds 40 tissue boxes. The dimensions of a tissue box are 4 inches by 6 inches by 3 inches. Which statements are true? Mark all that apply.

- (A) ● Each tissue box has a volume of 72 cubic inches.
- (B) Each container has a volume of about 1,440 cubic inches.
- (C) If a container could hold 48 tissue boxes, the volume of the container would be about 624 cubic inches.
- (D) ● If a container has a volume of 3,000 cubic inches, 41 tissue boxes will fit in the container.

5. A shipping container holds 40 gift boxes. The dimensions of a gift box are 4 inches by 5 inches by 2 inches. For numbers 5a–5c, choose the number that makes the statement true.

5a. Each gift box has a volume of [20 / (40) / 60] cubic inches.

5b. Each container has a volume of about [80 / 1,200 / (1,600)] cubic inches.

5c. If a container could hold 50 tissue boxes, the volume of the container would be about [1,000 / (2,000) / 3,000] cubic inches.

6. Miranda has cubes that measure 4 inches on each side. Which statements are true? Mark all that apply.

- (A) The volume of one cube is 48 cubic inches.
- (B) ● If Miranda fills a box with 12 cubes, the volume of the box is about 768 cubic inches.
- (C) If the volume of the box is 800 cubic inches, Miranda can fit 14 cubes in the box.
- (D) ● If the volume of the box is 1,000 cubes, Miranda can fit 15 cubes in the box.

STOP

Practice Test

5.MD.C.4 Geometric measurement: understand concepts of volume and relate volume to multiplication and to addition.

Name ______________________

1. Victoria used 1-inch cubes to build the rectangular prism shown. Find the volume of the rectangular prism Victoria built.

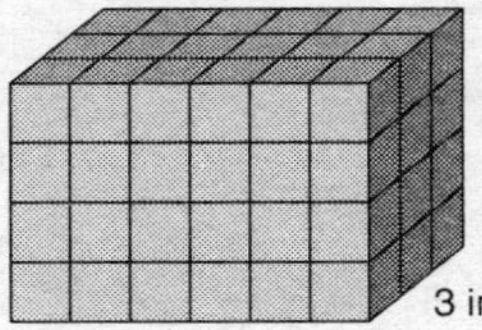

72 cubic inches

2. Carlton used 1-centimeter cubes to build the rectangular prism shown.

Find the volume of the rectangular prism Carlton built.

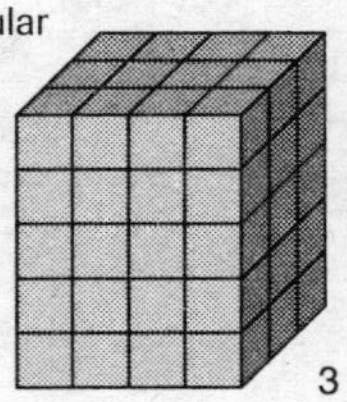

60 cubic inches

3. Ryan built a rectangular prism out of cubes.

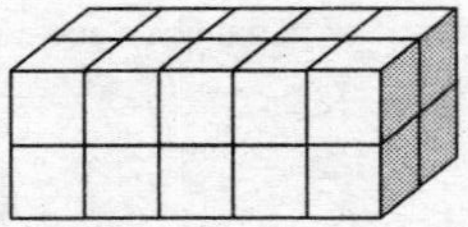

Part A

Find the volume of the prism.

$5 \times 2 \times 2 = 20$ cubic units

Part B

Ryan added 4 cubes to his prism. Calculate the volume. How has the volume changed?

$20 + 4 = 24$ cubic units; Possible explanation: The volume increased by 4.

GO ON

Practice Test

Name ______________________

4. Wendy used 1-centimeter cubes to build the rectangular prism shown. Find the volume of the rectangular prism Wendy built.

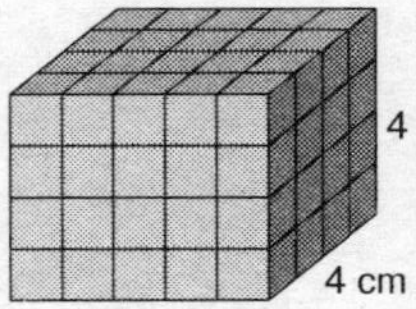

80 cubic centimeters

5. Carmen used 1-inch cubes to build the rectangular prism shown. Find the volume of the rectangular prism Carmen built.

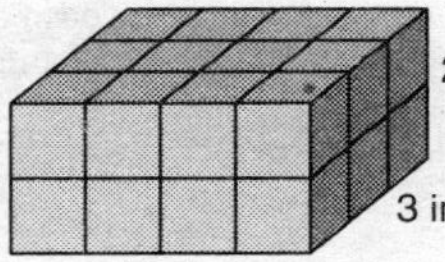

24 cubic inches

6. Julio built a rectangular prism out of cubes.

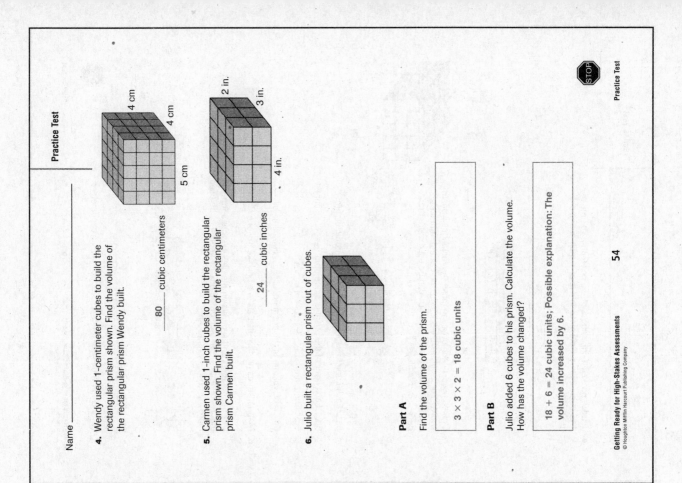

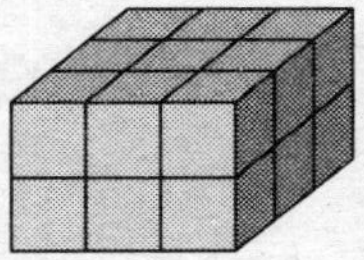

Part A

Find the volume of the prism.

$3 \times 3 \times 2 = 18$ cubic units

Part B

Julio added 6 cubes to his prism. Calculate the volume. How has the volume changed?

$18 + 6 = 24$ cubic units; Possible explanation: The volume increased by 6.

STOP

Name ______________________

1. Mark packed 1-inch cubes into a box with a volume of 120 cubic inches. How many layers of 1-inch cubes did Mark pack?

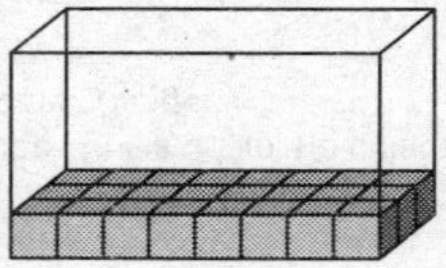

5 layers

2. Monica used 1-inch cubes to make the rectangular prism shown. For numbers 2a–2d, write the value from the tiles that makes each statement true. Each value can be used more than once or not at all.

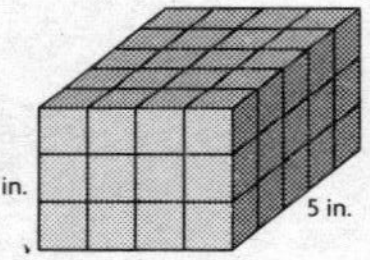

1	3	4	5	12	15	20	60

2a. Each cube has a volume of 1 cubic inch(es).

2b. Each layer of the prism is made up of 20 cubes.

2c. There are 3 layers of cubes.

2d. The volume of the prism is 60 cubic inches.

3. John used 1-inch cubes to make the rectangular prism shown. For numbers 3a–3d, write the value that makes each statement correct. Each value can be used more than once or not at all.

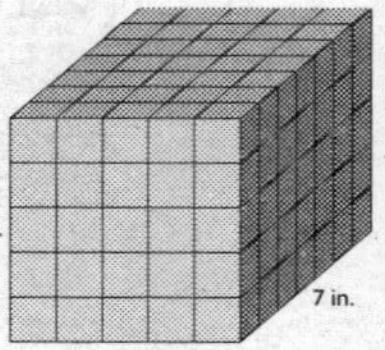

1	3	5	7	12	35	125	175

3a. Each cube has a volume of 1 cubic inch(es).

3b. Each layer of the prism is made up of 35 cubes.

3c. There are 5 layers of cubes.

3d. The volume of the prism is 175 cubic inches.

GO ON

Name ______________________

4. Jessica packed 1-inch cubes into a box with a volume of 144 cubic inches. How many layers of 1-inch cubes did Jessica pack?

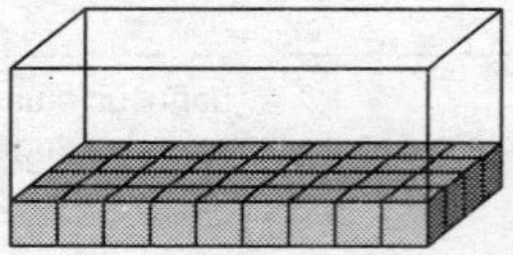

4 layers

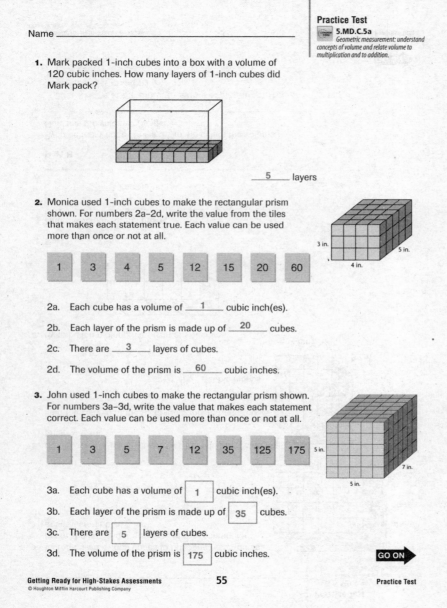

5. Donald used 1-inch cubes to make the rectangular prism shown. For numbers 5a–5d, write the value that makes each statement true. Each value can be used more than once or not at all.

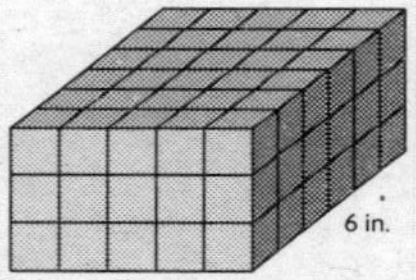

1	3	5	6	14	30	90	120

5a. Each cube has a volume of 1 cubic inch(es).

5b. Each layer of the prism is made up of 30 cubes.

5c. There are 3 layers of cubes.

5d. The volume of the prism is 90 cubic inches.

6. Manuel stores his favorite CDs in a box like the one shown.

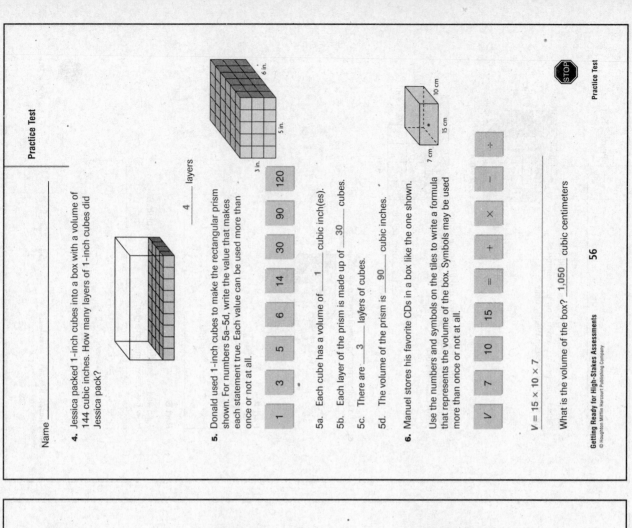

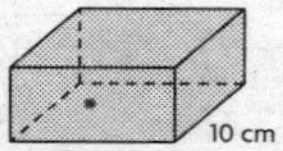

Use the numbers and symbols on the tiles to write a formula that represents the volume of the box. Symbols may be used more than once or not at all.

V	7	10	15	=	+	×	−	÷

$V = 15 \times 10 \times 7$

What is the volume of the box? 1,050 cubic centimeters

STOP

Name ____________

Practice Test

5.MD.C.5b *Geometric measurement: understand concepts of volume and relate volume to multiplication and to addition.*

1. Jose stores his baseball cards in a box like the one shown.

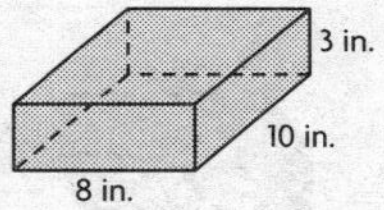

Use the numbers and symbols on the tiles to write a formula that represents the volume of the box. Symbols may be used more than once or not at all.

V	3	8	10	=	+	×	−	÷

$V = 8 \times 10 \times 3$

What is the volume of the box? 240 cubic inches

2. Megan's aquarium has a volume of 4,320 cubic inches. Which could be the dimensions of the aquarium? Mark all that apply.

- (A) 16 in. by 16 in. by 18 in.
- (B) 14 in. by 18 in. by 20 in.
- (C) 12 in. by 15 in. by 24 in. ●
- (D) 8 in. by 20 in. by 27 in. ●

3. Ken keeps paper clips in a box that is the shape of a cube. Each side of the cube is 3 inches. What is the volume of the box?

27 cubic inches

4. Tom keeps sticky notes in a box that is the shape of a cube. The box has a base of 16 square inches and a height of 4 inches. What is the volume of the box?

64 cubic inches

GO ON

Name ____________

Practice Test

5. Dakota's wading pool has a volume of 8,640 cubic inches. If her pool is a rectangular prism, which could be the dimensions of the wading pool? Mark all that apply.

- (A) Base: 360 square inches; Height: 24 inches ●
- (B) Base: 320 square inches; Height: 27 inches ●
- (C) Base: 403 square inches; Height: 28 inches
- (D) Base: 629 square inches; Height: 30 inches

6. Erin stores her photos in boxes like the one shown.

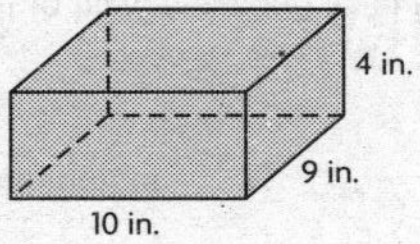

Use the numbers and symbols on the tiles to write a formula that represents the volume of one box. Symbols may be used more than once or not at all.

V	4	9	10	=	+	×	−	÷

$V = 10 \times 9 \times 4$

What is the combined volume of two boxes?

720 cubic inches

7. A shipping container has a volume of 2,880 cubic inches. Which could be the dimensions of the container? Mark all that apply.

- (A) 10 in. by 12 in. by 24 in. ●
- (B) 12 in. by 12 in. by 20 in. ●
- (C) 12 in. by 15 in. by 18 in.
- (D) 10 in. by 16 in. by 20 in.

STOP

Name ______________________

Practice Test

5.MD.C.5c
Geometric measurement: understand concepts of volume and relate volume to multiplication and to addition.

1. Jason builds steps using 2 pieces of wood with the same height and width but different lengths. What is the volume of the steps he builds?

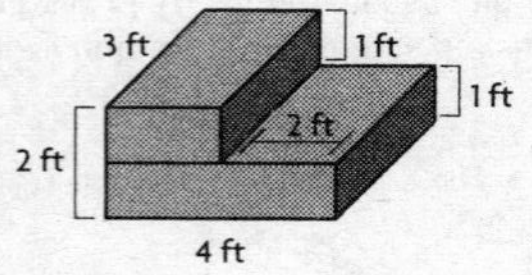

18 cubic feet

2. Fabio glues 2 rectangular blocks together to make a model chair for a doll house. What is the volume of the model?

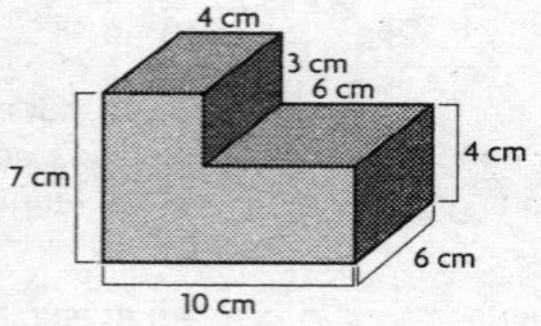

Volume = 312 cubic centimeters

3. Amelia stacks a moving box on top of a larger box. Both boxes have the same width. What is the combined volume of the boxes?

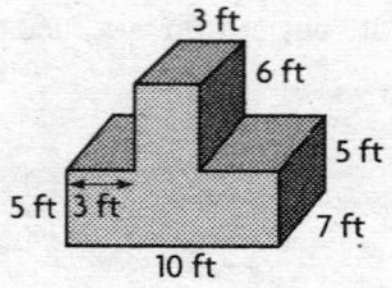

Volume = 476 cubic feet

GO ON

Name ______________________

Practice Test

4. Diane places 2 drawers with the same width and height on top of each other. What is the combined volume of the 2 drawers?

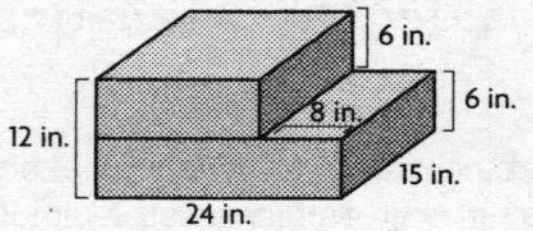

3,600 cubic inches

5. Tomas makes a letter T using 2 foam blocks. What is the volume of the shape Tomas makes?

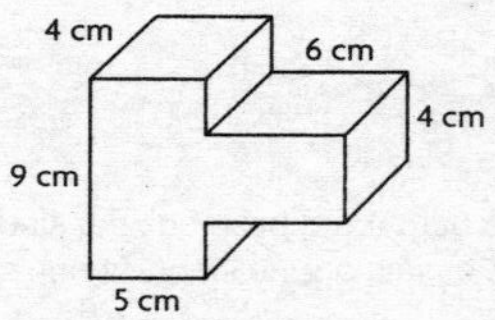

Volume = 276 cubic centimeters

6. The stage at a stadium is built to have a second level for a drum set. Harvey wants to find the combined volume of the 2 rectangular prisms that make up the stage. First write the lengths of the 2 missing dimensions. Then use a formula and calculate the volume of the stage.

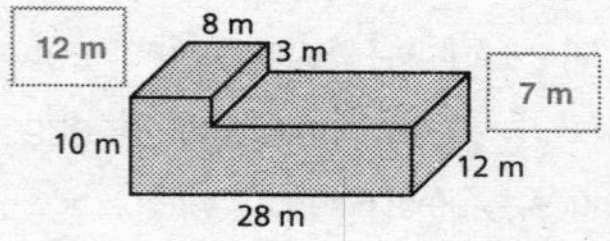

2,640 cubic meters; Possible equation: $V = 8 \times 12 \times 10 + 20 \times 12 \times 7$

STOP

Name ______________________

Practice Test

5.G.A.1
Graph points on the coordinate plane to solve real-world and mathematical problems.

1. The letters on the coordinate grid represent the locations of the first four holes on a golf course. Which of the following accurately describes the location of a hole? Mark all that apply.

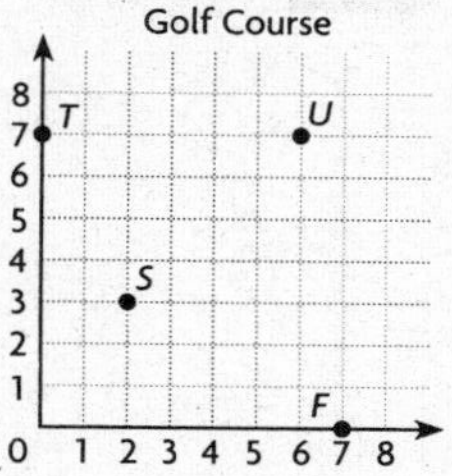

   - (A) Hole *U* is 4 units left and 4 units down from hole *S*.
   - (B) Hole *F* is 1 unit right and 7 units down from hole *U*.
   - (C) Hole *T* is 2 units left and 4 units up from hole *S*.
   - (D) Hole *S* is 3 units left and 5 units up from hole *F*.

2. Lindsey made a map of her town. Match each location below with the correct ordered pair that marks it on the coordinate grid. Not every ordered pair will be used.

Clock Tower	(4, 4)
	(4, 1)
Art Museum	(1, 3)
	(5, 4)
East Park	(4, 5)
	(3, 1)
Movie Theater	(2, 4)
	(1, 4)
School	(4, 2)

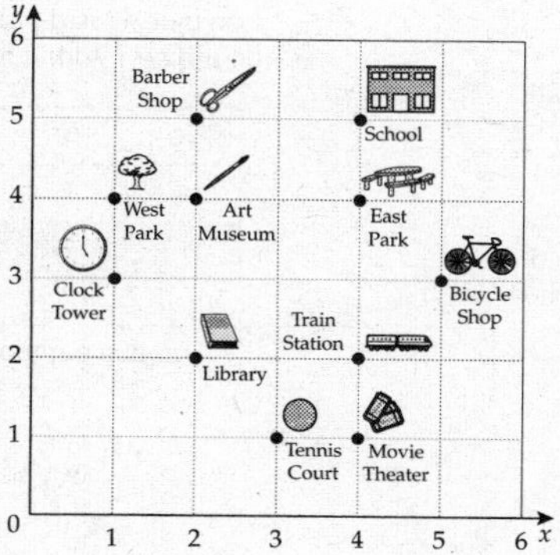

3. Lucy's house is located at the point shown on the coordinate grid. Ainsley's house is located 2 units right and 3 units down from Lucy's house. Plot a point on the coordinate grid to represent the location of Ainsley's house.

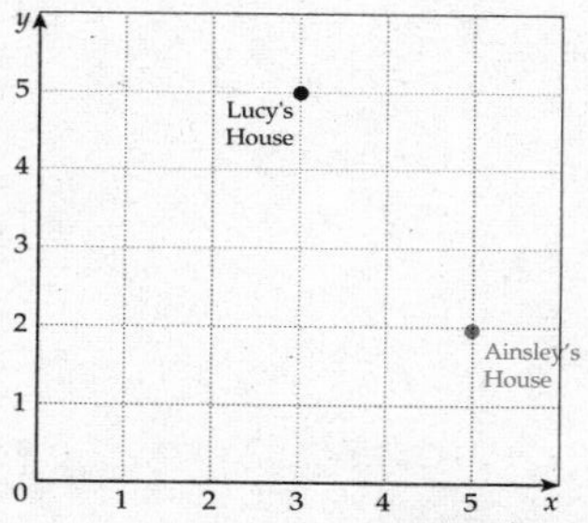

   What ordered pair represents the location of Lucy's house? (3, 5)

   What ordered pair represents the location of Ainsley's house? (5, 2)

GO ON

Name ______________________

Practice Test

4. The map shows the locations of attractions at an amusement park. Match each location below with the correct ordered pair that marks it on the map. Not every ordered pair will be used.

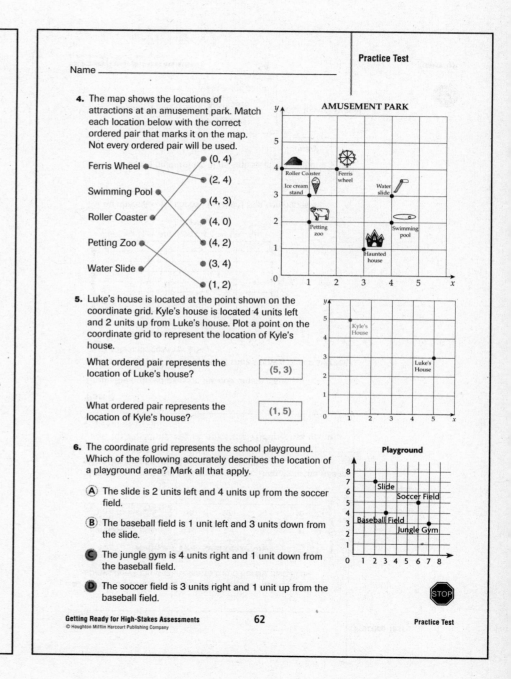

	(0, 4)
Ferris Wheel	(2, 4)
Swimming Pool	(4, 3)
Roller Coaster	(4, 0)
Petting Zoo	(4, 2)
Water Slide	(3, 4)
	(1, 2)

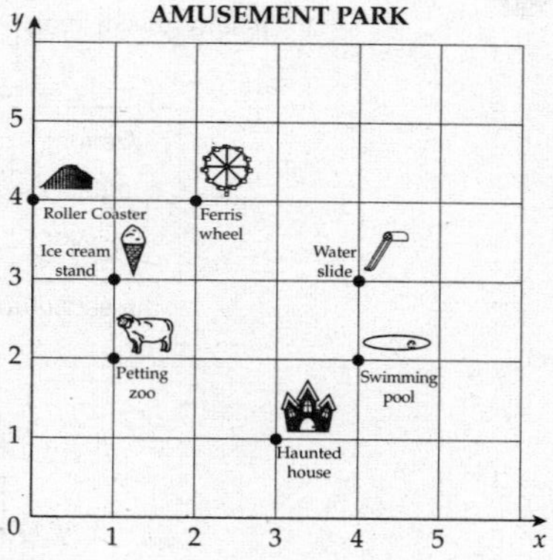

5. Luke's house is located at the point shown on the coordinate grid. Kyle's house is located 4 units left and 2 units up from Luke's house. Plot a point on the coordinate grid to represent the location of Kyle's house.

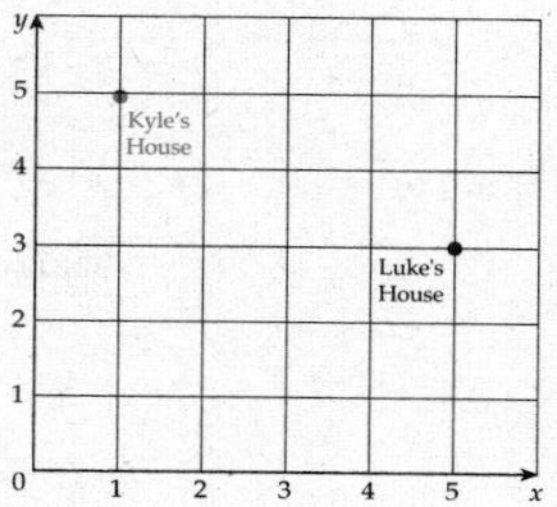

   What ordered pair represents the location of Luke's house? (5, 3)

   What ordered pair represents the location of Kyle's house? (1, 5)

6. The coordinate grid represents the school playground. Which of the following accurately describes the location of a playground area? Mark all that apply.

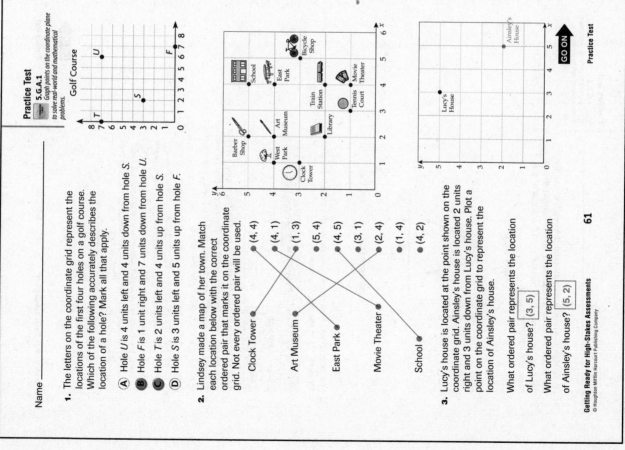

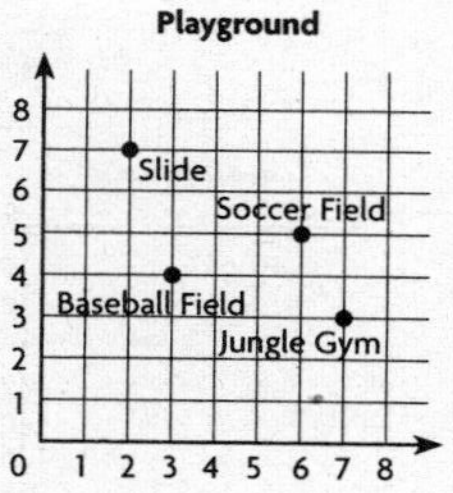

   - (A) The slide is 2 units left and 4 units up from the soccer field.
   - (B) The baseball field is 1 unit left and 3 units down from the slide.
   - (C) The jungle gym is 4 units right and 1 unit down from the baseball field.
   - (D) The soccer field is 3 units right and 1 unit up from the baseball field.

STOP

Name ______________________

Practice Test

5.G.A.2 *Graph points on the coordinate plane to solve real-world and mathematical problems.*

1. For 6 days in a row, Julia measured the depth of the snow in a shaded area of her backyard. The line graph shows her data. Between which two days did the depth of the snow decrease the most?

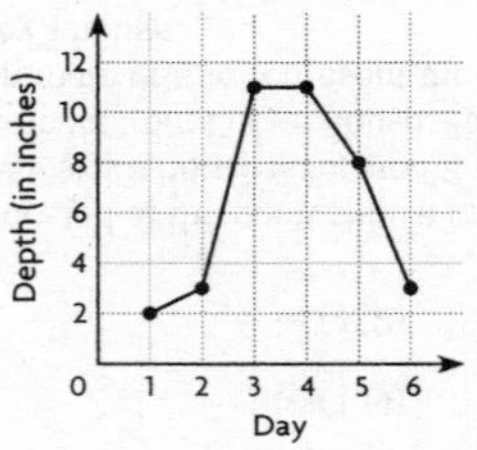

between Day **5** and Day **6**

2. The table shows how much a puppy weighs from the age of 1 month old to the age of 5 months old.

Puppy's Weight					
Age (in months)	1	2	3	4	5
Weight (in pounds)	12	18	23	31	34

What ordered pairs would you plot to show the puppy's weight on a coordinate grid? How do you think the ordered pairs would be different if the puppy's weight was measured every week instead of every month? Explain your reasoning.

(1, 12), (2, 18), (3, 23), (4, 31), (5, 34); Possible answer: There would be many more ordered pairs since there would be several weight measurements per month. Also, the puppy's weight would not increase as fast since it would not gain as much weight in a week as it does in a month.

GO ON

Name ______________________

Practice Test

3. Randy is training for a race. She makes a table that shows how long it takes her to run different distances.

Running Time and Distance				
Number of Miles	1	2	3	4
Time (in minutes)	10	20	30	40

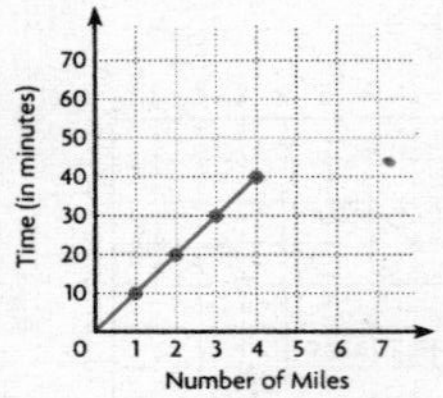

Part A

Write the number pairs as ordered pairs. Then write the rule to describe how the number pairs are related.

(1, 10), (2, 20), (3, 30), (4, 40); Rule: Multiply the number of miles by 10.

Part B

Graph the ordered pairs on the coordinate plane.

4. A scientist made a line graph that shows how a bear's average heart rate changes over time.

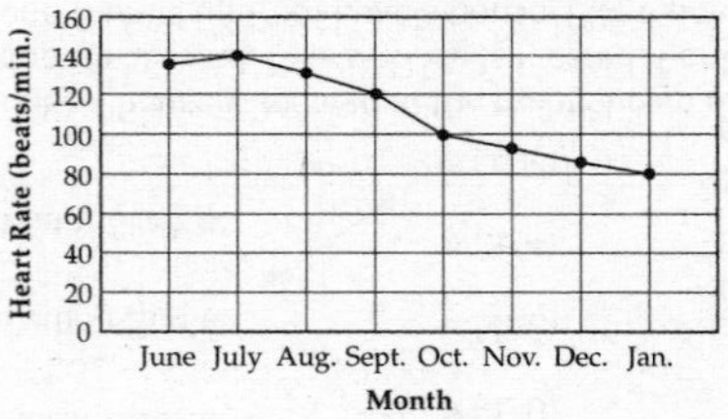

For numbers 4a–4b, choose the word that completes the statement.

4a. The bear's heart rate is at its highest in [July (circled) / October / January].

4b. The bear's heart rate [increases / decreases (circled) / stays the same] from July to August.

STOP

Name ______________________

Practice Test
5.G.B.3
Classify two-dimensional figures into categories based on their properties.

1. Mr. Delgado sees this sign while he is driving. For numbers 1a–1b, choose the values and term that correctly describe the shape Mr. Delgado saw.

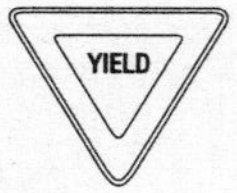

1a. The figure has [**(3)** / 4 / 5] sides and [0 / 2 / **(3)**] vertices.

1b. All of the sides are congruent, so the figure is [not a polygon / **(a regular polygon)** / not a regular polygon].

2. Javier drew the shape shown. For numbers 2a–2b, choose the values and term that correctly describe the shape Javier drew.

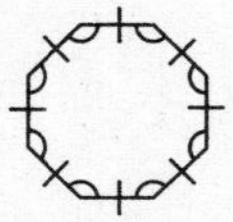

2a. The figure has [6 / 7 / **(8)**] sides and [6 / **(8)** / 12] angles.

2b. The figure is a [**(regular octagon)** / regular heptagon / regular quadrilateral].

3. For numbers 3a–3c, write the name of one quadrilateral from the tiles to complete a true statement. Use each quadrilateral only once.

Tiles: square, trapezoid, rectangle

3a. A **rectangle** is always a parallelogram.

3b. A **square** is always a rhombus.

3c. A **trapezoid** is sometimes a parallelogram.

GO ON

Name ______________________

Practice Test

4. Mario is making a diagram that shows the relationship between different kinds of quadrilaterals. In the diagram, each quadrilateral on a lower level can also be described by the quadrilateral(s) above it on higher levels.

Part A

Complete the diagram by writing the name of one figure from the tiles in each box. Not every figure will be used.

quadrilateral
↓
trapezoid
↓
parallelogram
↓
rhombus
↓
square

Tiles: trapezoid, triangle, rhombus, parallelogram

Part B

Mario claims that a rhombus is *sometimes* a square, but a square is *always* a rhombus. Is he correct? Explain your answer.

Yes; Possible explanation: A square has 4 sides that are congruent and equal. A square with these features is also a rhombus. However, when a rhombus does not have 90 degree angles, it is not a square.

5. Kayla drew the shape shown. For numbers 5a–5b, choose the values and term that correctly describe the shape Kayla drew.

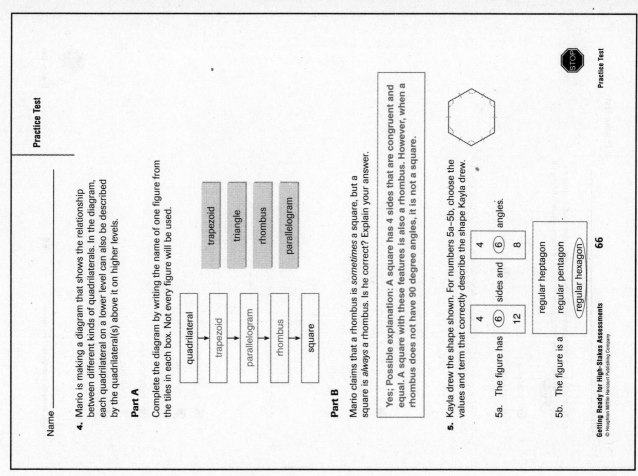

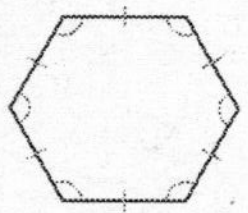

5a. The figure has [4 / **(6)** / 12] sides and [4 / **(6)** / 8] angles.

5b. The figure is a [regular heptagon / regular pentagon / **(regular hexagon)**].

STOP

Name ______________________

Practice Test
5.G.B.4
Classify two-dimensional figures into categories based on their properties.

1. Fran drew a triangle with no congruent sides and 1 right angle. Which term accurately describes the triangle? Mark all that apply.

(A) isosceles
(B) scalene
(C) acute
(D) right

2. Nathan drew a design with scalene, obtuse triangles. Which figures could be the triangles Nathan drew? Mark all that apply.

(A) 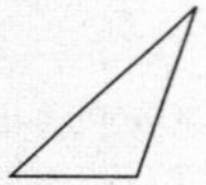

(B) 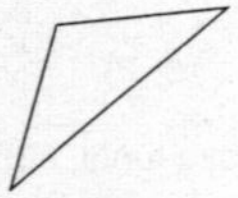

(C) 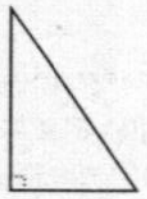

3. Kelly drew a triangle with exactly 2 congruent sides and 3 acute angles. Which of the following accurately describes the triangle? Mark all that apply.

(A) isosceles
(B) acute
(C) obtuse
(D) equilateral

GO ON

Name ______________________

Practice Test

4. Kristin drew a triangle with 2 congruent sides and 1 obtuse angle. Which term accurately describes the triangle? Mark all that apply.

(A) isosceles
(B) scalene
(C) acute
(D) obtuse

5. Natalie drew an acute, isosceles triangle. Which figure could be Natalie's triangle?

(A) 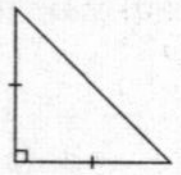

(B) 

(C) 

6. Which names apply to the polygon? Mark all that apply.

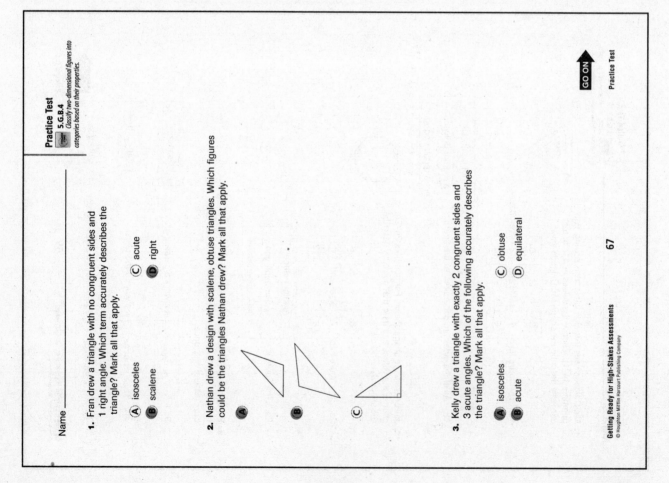

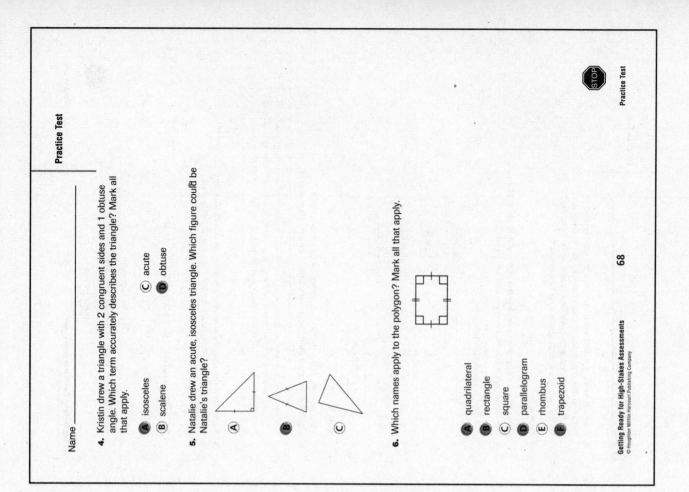

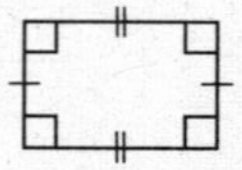

(A) quadrilateral
(B) rectangle
(C) square
(D) parallelogram
(E) rhombus
(F) trapezoid

STOP

Name ____________

Beginning-of-Year Test
Page 1

1. Find the property that each equation shows. Write the equation in the correct box.

$11 \times (4 \times 6) = (11 \times 4) \times 6$	$14 + 27 + 18 = 27 + 14 + 18$
$15 + (12 + 11) = (15 + 12) + 11$	$18 \times 2 = 2 \times 18$
$5 \times 1 = 5$	$72 + 0 = 72$

Commutative Property of Multiplication $18 \times 2 = 2 \times 18$	Associative Property of Addition $15 + (12 + 11) = (15 + 12) + 11$	Identity Property of Addition $72 + 0 = 72$
Commutative Property of Addition $14 + 27 + 18 = 27 + 14 + 18$	Associative Property of Multiplication $11 \times (4 \times 6) = (11 \times 4) \times 6$	Identity Property of Multiplication $5 \times 1 = 5$

2. 3.67 is 10 times as much as [0.367 (circled) / 3.67 / 36.7 / 367] and $\frac{1}{10}$ of [0.367 / 3.67 / 36.7 (circled) / 367]

3. Mario is making dinner for 9 people. Mario buys 6 containers of soup. Each container is 18 ounces. If everyone gets the same amount of soup, how much soup will each person get?

12 ounces

GO ON

Name ____________

Beginning-of-Year Test
Page 2

4. Jason used large blocks for an art project. What is the volume of the shape he made?

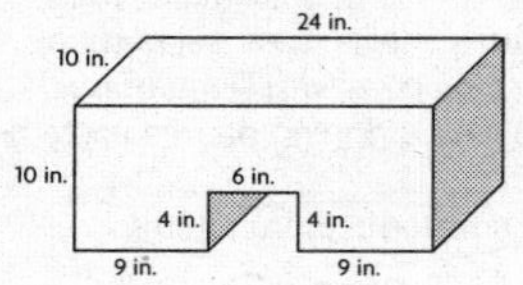

2,160 cubic inches

5. 0.2 [< / > / = (circled)] two tenths

6. For numbers 6a–6d, tell which expressions require you to rename mixed numbers before you can subtract. Find each difference. Write each expression and the difference in the correct box.

6a. $5\frac{2}{5} - 2\frac{1}{4}$

6b. $5 - 2\frac{7}{8}$

6c. $7\frac{2}{3} - 6\frac{1}{8}$

6d. $9\frac{1}{6} - 5\frac{2}{3}$

Requires Renaming	Does Not Require Renaming
$5 - 2\frac{7}{8} = 2\frac{1}{8}$ $9\frac{1}{6} - 5\frac{2}{3} = 3\frac{1}{2}$	$5\frac{2}{5} - 2\frac{1}{4} = 3\frac{3}{20}$ $7\frac{2}{3} - 6\frac{1}{8} = 1\frac{13}{24}$

7. The table shows the equations Mr. Berger discussed in math class today.

Equations
$4 \times 10^0 = 4$
$4 \times 10^1 = 40$
$4 \times 10^2 = 400$
$4 \times 10^3 = 4{,}000$

Explain the pattern of zeros in the product when multiplying by powers of 10.

Possible explanation: For each power of ten, the number of zeros written after the base is the same as the number in the exponent.

GO ON

8. Ursula mixed $3\frac{1}{8}$ cups of dry ingredients with $1\frac{2}{5}$ cups of liquid ingredients. For numbers 8a–8c, estimate the amount of ingredients Ursula used. Choose the correct benchmarks and sum.

8a. Ursula used about [2 / (3) / $3\frac{1}{2}$ / 4] cups of dry ingredients.

8b. Ursula used about [1 / ($1\frac{1}{2}$) / $1\frac{3}{4}$ / 2] cup(s) of liquid ingredients.

8c. Ursula used about [3 / $3\frac{1}{2}$ / 4 / ($4\frac{1}{2}$)] cups of ingredients.

9. Tommy has 5 jars of marbles. Each jar is $\frac{2}{3}$ filled with marbles. How many jars of marbles does Tommy have? Shade the model and complete the calculations to show how you found your answer.

$5 \times \frac{2}{3} = \frac{\boxed{10}}{3} = \underline{3\frac{1}{3}}$ jars of marbles

10. Write 247.903 in expanded form.

200 + 40 + 7 + 0.9 + 0.003

GO ON

11. Stacey worked on her garden for $4\frac{3}{4}$ hours. Josh worked on his garden $\frac{2}{3}$ times as long as Stacey. Vicki worked on her garden $1\frac{3}{8}$ times as long as Stacey. Which statements are true? Mark all that apply.

- (A) ● Stacey worked longer on her garden than Josh worked on his garden.
- (B) ● Stacey spent less time working on her garden than Vicki spent on her garden.
- (C) Josh worked longer on his garden than Vicki worked on her garden.
- (D) Stacey worked in her garden more than Josh and Vicki.

12. Ten pounds of rice are distributed equally into 6 bags to give out at the food bank. How many pounds of rice are in each bag?

$\frac{5}{3}$ or $1\frac{2}{3}$ pounds

13. Mr. Diaz is building a fence around his yard. For numbers 13a–13b, choose the values and term that correctly describe the shape of Mr. Diaz's fence.

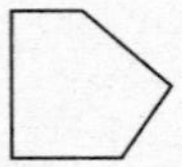

13a. The figure has [3 / 4 / (5)] sides and [0 / (5) / 6] vertices.

13b. None of the sides are congruent, so the figure is [a regular polygon / not a polygon / (not a regular polygon)].

14. Erica earned 30,000 bonus points on her computer assignment. This is 10 times as many points as she earned last week. How many bonus points did Erica earn last week?

3,000 points

GO ON

15. Use the numbers to complete the ordered pairs that represent the endpoints of line segment *RT*.

2	3
5	8
9	10

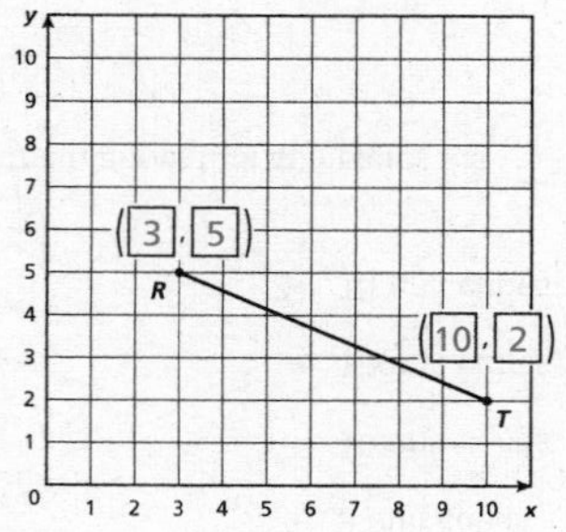

16. A small stadium can sell up to 6,768 tickets per event.

Part A

If tickets sold out for 143 baseball games, how many tickets were sold for those games in all?

967,824 tickets

Part B

The stadium also hosts concerts. If tickets sold out for 102 concerts, how many tickets were sold for the concerts in all?

690,336 tickets

17. Flora bought 4.13 pounds of tuna salad and 2.7 pounds of chicken salad. Which statement is true?

- Ⓐ (marked) Rounded to the nearest whole number, Flora bought 4 pounds of tuna salad.
- Ⓑ Rounded to the nearest tenth, Flora bought 4.3 pounds of tuna salad.
- Ⓒ Rounded to the nearest whole number, Flora bought 2 pounds of chicken salad.

GO ON

18. Your teacher gives you the problem $5 \div \frac{1}{4}$.

Part A

Write a story problem to represent $5 \div \frac{1}{4}$. **Check students' story problems.**

Possible problem: Sam has 5 feet of string. He cuts the string into pieces that are $\frac{1}{4}$ foot long. How many pieces of string does he have now?

Part B

Use a related multiplication expression to solve your story problem. Show your work.

$5 \div \frac{1}{4} = 5 \times 4 = 20$; 20 pieces

19. Marie plants flowers in a planter that is $1\frac{1}{2}$ feet long and $1\frac{2}{3}$ feet wide. She plans to cover the entire area with fertilizer. How much area will she need to spread with fertilizer? Draw a rectangle to help you solve.

Check students' models.

$2\frac{1}{2}$ square feet

20. Rowanda jogged 2.14 kilometers farther than Terrance. Select the values that could represent how far each student jogged. Mark all that apply.

- Ⓐ (marked) Rowanda: 6.5 km, Terrance: 4.36 km
- Ⓑ Rowanda: 4.8 km, Terrance: 2.76 km
- Ⓒ Rowanda: 3.51 km, Terrance: 5.65 km
- Ⓓ (marked) Rowanda: 7.24 km, Terrance: 5.1 km

GO ON

Name ______________________

21. Without multiplying, classify each product as being less than $\frac{3}{5}$, equal to $\frac{3}{5}$, or greater than $\frac{3}{5}$. Write the letter of each expression in the correct box.

A $\frac{3}{5} \times \frac{1}{2}$ **B** $\frac{3}{5} \times \frac{2}{3}$ **C** $\frac{3}{5} \times \frac{5}{4}$ **D** $\frac{3}{5} \times \frac{3}{1}$ **E** $\frac{3}{5} \times \frac{7}{7}$ **F** $\frac{3}{5} \times 2$

Less Than $\frac{3}{5}$	Equal to $\frac{3}{5}$	Greater Than $\frac{3}{5}$
A, B	E	C, D, F

22. Jerome filled bags with trail mix. The weights of the bags are $\frac{1}{8}$-lb, $\frac{1}{4}$-lb, $\frac{1}{4}$-lb, $\frac{1}{2}$-lb, $\frac{1}{8}$-lb, $\frac{1}{4}$-lb, $\frac{3}{8}$-lb, $\frac{1}{2}$-lb, $\frac{1}{8}$-lb, $\frac{1}{4}$-lb, $\frac{1}{8}$-lb, $\frac{1}{4}$-lb, $\frac{1}{8}$-lb, $\frac{1}{8}$-lb, $\frac{1}{4}$-lb, and $\frac{3}{8}$-lb. Organize the information in a line plot.

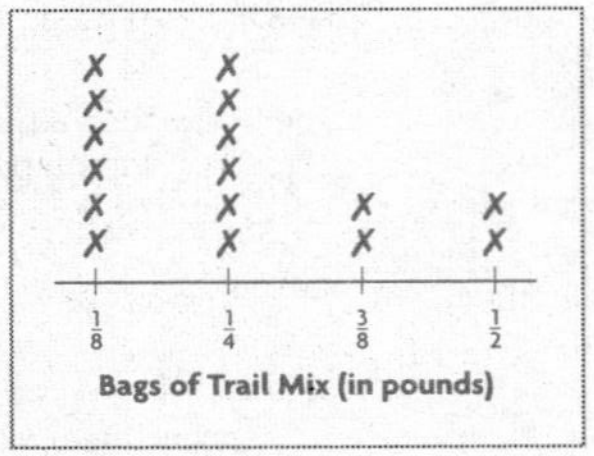

What is the average weight of the bags?

$\frac{1}{4}$ pound(s)

23. Match the figure with the number of unit cubes that would be needed to build each figure. Not every number of unit cubes will be used.

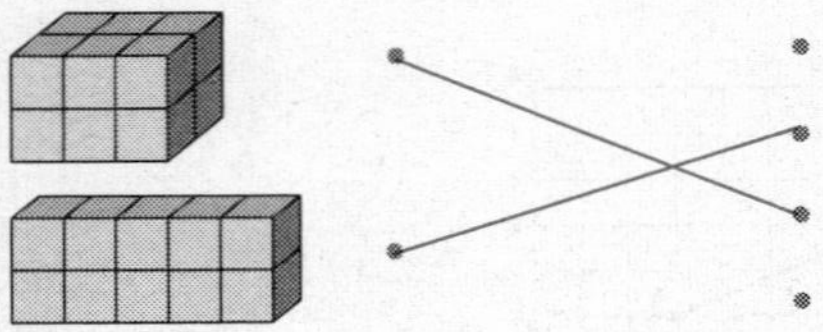

- 9 unit cubes
- 10 unit cubes
- 12 unit cubes
- 15 unit cubes

24. For numbers 24a–24c, write the number that completes the equation.

24a. $6 \div \boxed{\frac{1}{2}} = 12$

24b. $\frac{1}{3} \div \boxed{8} = \frac{1}{24}$

24c. $4 \div \frac{1}{7} = \boxed{28}$

GO ON

Name ______________________

25. A shipping container holds 36 shoe boxes. The dimensions of a shoebox are 4 inches by 5 inches by 8 inches. What is the volume of the shipping container? Explain how you found your answer.

5,760 cubic inches; Possible explanation: I multiplied $5 \times 4 \times 8 = 160$ to find the volume of one shoebox. Then I multiplied 160×36 to find the volume of the container.

26. Darnell used 1-centimeter cubes to build the rectangular prism shown. Find the volume of the rectangular prism Darnell built.

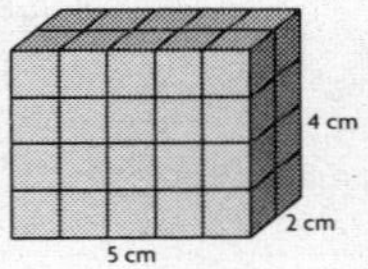

<u>40</u> cubic centimeters

27. Marsha packed 1-inch cubes into a box with a volume of 36 cubic inches. How many layers of 1-inch cubes did Marsha pack?

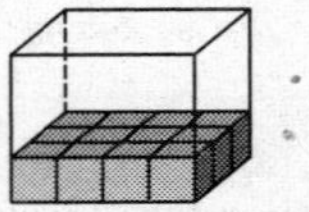

<u>3</u> layers

28. Kristin drew a triangle with 3 congruent sides and 3 congruent angles. Which term accurately describes the triangle? Mark all that apply.

- (A) equilateral (marked)
- (B) scalene
- (C) acute (marked)
- (D) obtuse

GO ON

Name ____________________

Party Planning

Tanisha is planning a backyard party. She will serve hamburgers, potato salad, strawberry shortcake, and lemonade. Including Tanisha, 28 people will be at the party. Use this information to help Tanisha plan her party. Show your work. Round all dollar amounts to the nearest cent (nearest hundredth).

1. a. Tanisha's potato salad recipe calls for 2.5 pounds of potatoes. She decides to make 3.5 times her regular recipe. How many pounds of potatoes should Tanisha buy? Show your work.

$3.5 \times 2.5 = 8.75$

Tanisha should buy 8.75 pounds of potatoes.

b. Potatoes are sold in 2.25-pound bags. How many whole bags must Tanisha buy in order to have enough potatoes?

$8.75 \div 2.25 = 3.89$

Tanisha must buy 4 whole bags.

c. Potatoes cost $0.62 per pound. What is the total cost of the bags of potatoes Tanisha needs to buy?

$2.25 \times 0.62 = 1.395$

$1.395 \times 4 = 5.58$

The bags of potatoes cost a total of $ 5.58.

GO ON

Name ____________________

2. a. Tanisha uses 2.88 pounds of ground beef to make 8 same-size hamburgers. How many pounds of ground beef are in each hamburger?

$2.88 \div 8 = 0.36$

There are 0.36 pounds of ground beef in each hamburger.

b. Tanisha wants to make 1 hamburger for each of the 28 people at the party. How many pounds of ground beef does Tanisha need?

$28 \times 0.36 = 10.08$

Tanisha needs 10.08 pounds of ground beef.

3. Tanisha spends $20.25 on 9 quarts of strawberries for the shortcake. What is the price of each quart of strawberries?

$20.25 \div 9 = 2.25$

The price for each quart of strawberries is $ 2.25.

GO ON

4. Tanisha expects that each person will drink two 8-ounce glasses of lemonade at the party. Write an expression to show the words. How many ounces of lemonade does Tanisha need to make?

Possible expression: $28 \times (2 \times 8) = 448$

448 ounces

5. Tanisha's mother buys 38 lemons. They know it takes 8 lemons to make 80 ounces of lemonade. Does Tanisha need more lemons? If not, how many extra lemons does she have? If so, how many more lemons does she need? Explain how you found your answer.

Yes, Tanisha needs 7 more lemons; Possible explanation: I divided 80 ounces by 8 to find how many ounces 1 lemon makes. 1 lemon makes 10 ounces. I divided 448, the total number of ounces needed, by 10 to find how many lemons Tanisha needed. $448 \div 10 = 44.8$. I need a whole number of lemons so I rounded to 45 and subtracted the amount of lemons Tanisha already had. $45 - 38 = 7$

GO ON

6. Tanisha makes a budget to keep track of her spending on party food. Fill in the blanks in the budget table. Some of the answers will come from questions 1–5.

Item	Amount	Cost of 1 Unit	Total Cost
Potatoes	9 lb	$0.62/lb	$ **5.58**
Hamburger	**10.08** lb	$ **2.00** /lb	$20.16
Strawberries	9 qt	$ **2.25** /qt	$20.25
Lemons	**45 lemons**	$0.12/lemon	$ **5.40**

a. What is the total cost of food for the party?

$5.58 + 20.16 + 20.25 + 5.40 = \$51.39$

b. If you split the cost of food evenly among the 28 people, what is the cost of food for 1 person?

$51.39 \div 28 = \$1.84$

c. Tanisha's party food budget is $60.00. How many more people can she afford to invite to the party? Explain your reasoning.

4 more people; Possible explanation: I subtracted the cost of food for 28 people from Tanisha's budget, $60 - 51.39 = \$8.61$. Then I subtracted the cost of food for 1 person four times, $8.61 - 1.84 - 1.84 - 1.84 - 1.84 = \$1.25$. She doesn't have enough money to invite a fifth person.

STOP

Fluency with Whole Numbers and Decimals

Party Planning

COMMON CORE STANDARDS

5.NBT.B.7	Add, subtract, multiply, and divide decimals to hundredths, using concrete models or drawings and strategies based on place value, properties of operations, and/or the relationship between addition and subtraction; relate the strategy to a written method and explain the reasoning used.
5.OA.A.2	Write simple expressions that record calculations with numbers, and interpret numerical expressions without evaluating them.
MP1	Make sense of problems and persevere in solving them.

Also 5.NBT.A.1, 5.NBT.A.2, 5.NBT.A.3, 5.NBT.B.5, 5.NBT.B.6, 5.OA.A.1, MP3, MP4, MP7, MP8

PURPOSE

To assess the ability to represent and solve problems by writing and evaluating expressions with multi-digit whole numbers and with decimals to the hundredths place

TIME

40–45 minutes

GROUPING

Individuals

MATERIALS

- Performance Task, paper, pencil

PREPARATION HINTS

- Review whole-number and decimal operations with students before assigning the task.
- Review vocabulary, including *round*, *hundredth*, and *budget*.

IMPLEMENTATION NOTES

- Read the task aloud to students and make sure that all students have a clear understanding of the task.
- Students may use manipulatives to complete the task.
- Allow students as much paper as they need to complete the task.
- Allow as much time as students need to complete the task.
- Students must complete the task individually, without collaboration.
- Collect all student work when the task is complete.

TASK SUMMARY

Students write and solve expressions involving operations with multi-digit whole numbers and decimals to hundredths. They use these expressions to plan, prepare, and pay for the food for a backyard party.

REPRESENTATION

In this task teachers can…

- Provide options for comprehension by linking to prior knowledge of shopping for food and hosting parties.
- Increase accessibility of text with diagrams, charts, and illustrations.

ACTION and EXPRESSION

In this task teachers can…

- Support students' executive functioning by creating and displaying a schedule for working through the task.

ENGAGEMENT

In this task, teachers can…

- Sustain efforts and persistence by providing predictable breaks.
- Increase mastery by providing feedback that emphasizes student effort and improvement.

EXPECTED STUDENT OUTCOMES

- Complete the task within the time allowed
- Reflect engagement in a productive struggle
- Write and solve expressions with multi-digit whole numbers and decimals to the hundredths place

SCORING

Use the associated Rubric to evaluate each student's work.

Performance Task Rubric

PARTY PLANNING	
A level 3 response	• Shows that the student has made sense of the task and persevered • Indicates that the student can construct viable arguments • Shows ability to write and evaluate expressions to solve word problems • Performs operations, compares, orders, and rounds multi-digit whole numbers and decimals to hundredths place
A level 2 response	• Shows that the student has made sense of the task and persevered • Indicates that the student can construct viable arguments • Shows an ability to write and evaluate expressions to solve word problems • Shows an ability to perform operations, compares, orders, and rounds multi-digit whole numbers and decimals to hundredths place • Addresses most or all aspects of the task using mathematically sound procedures • May contain an incorrect answer derived from a correct procedure
A level 1 response	• Shows that the student has made sense of at least some components of the task • Shows attempts to construct viable arguments • Shows uneven ability to write and evaluate expressions to solve word problems • Shows little ability to perform operations, compares, orders, and rounds multi-digit whole numbers and decimals to hundredths place
A level 0 response	• Shows little evidence that the student has made sense of the problems within the task • Shows an inability to construct viable arguments • Shows little or no ability to write and evaluate expressions to solve word problems • Shows little or no ability to perform operations, compare, order, and round multi-digit whole numbers and decimals to hundredths place • Shows little evidence of adequately addressing all parts of the task • Shows little evidence of applying mathematics correctly or appropriately to the situation

Name ____________________

1. Kari, Jason, and Julia joined a fitness program in which they track how much they exercise. The table below shows the distances they ran last week.

Name	Miles Run
Kari	$6\frac{3}{4}$
Jason	$8\frac{1}{3}$
Julia	$5\frac{1}{2}$

This week, Kari plans to run $1\frac{1}{2}$ times longer than last week. Jason plans to run $\frac{3}{4}$ as far as he ran last week. Julia plans to run $1\frac{1}{3}$ times as far as she ran last week. Match each student's name to the number of hours he or she plans to run this week.

Student	Miles This Week
Kari	$7\frac{1}{3}$
Jason	$10\frac{1}{8}$
Julia	$6\frac{1}{4}$

(Answer: Kari — $10\frac{1}{8}$; Jason — $6\frac{1}{4}$; Julia — $7\frac{1}{3}$)

2. Select other ways to write 60.472. Mark all that apply.

- **(A)** $(6 \times 10) + (4 \times 0.1) + (7 \times 0.01) + (2 \times 0.001)$
- **(B)** $60 + 0.4 + 0.07 + 0.002$
- **(C)** sixty and four hundred seventy-two thousandths
- (D) sixty-four and seventy-two thousandths

3. Multiply. Show your work.

510×17

Check students' work.

$510 \times 17 = 8{,}670$

GO ON

Name ____________________

4. What is the volume of the rectangular prism?

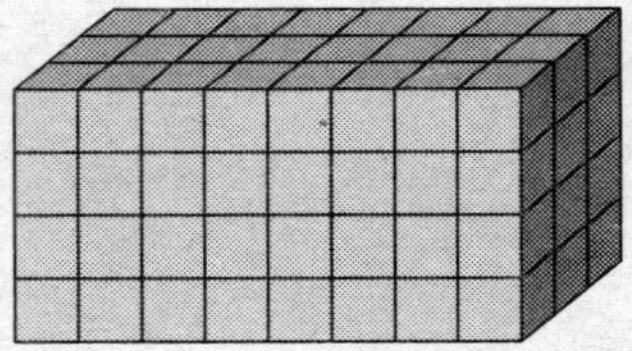

96 cubic units

5. 0.3 [< / **(>)** / =] three hundredths

6. What is the sum of $\frac{3}{5}$ and $\frac{2}{3}$?

Find equivalent fractions to help you add.

$\boxed{\frac{9}{15}} + \boxed{\frac{10}{15}}$

$\frac{3}{5} + \frac{2}{3} = \boxed{\frac{19}{15} \text{ or } 1\frac{4}{15}}$

7. The Space Needle in Seattle, Washington, is 184.41 meters tall. What is another way to show 184.41? Mark all that apply.

- (A) $100 + 800 + 4 + 0.04 + 0.1$
- **(B)** one hundred eighty-four and forty-one hundredths
- **(C)** $(1 \times 100) + (8 \times 10) + (4 \times 1) + (4 \times 0.1) + (1 \times 0.01)$

GO ON

Name ____________________

8. It takes Evan $6\frac{3}{4}$ hours to mow 3 lawns. It takes him $2\frac{1}{3}$ hours to mow Mr. Gal's lawn and $1\frac{3}{4}$ hours to mow Ms. Lee's lawn. How many hours does it take Evan to mow the third lawn? Use the numbers and symbols to write an equation that represents the problem. Then solve the equation. Symbols may be used more than once or not at all.

$6\frac{3}{4}$	$2\frac{1}{3}$	$1\frac{3}{4}$	X	=	+

Possible answer: $6\frac{3}{4} = 2\frac{1}{3} + 1\frac{3}{4} + X$

Time needed to mow the third lawn: $2\frac{2}{3}$ hours

9. Jesse surveyed $\frac{3}{4}$ of the students at her school. Of those surveyed, $\frac{2}{3}$ participate in a school club or sports team. What fraction of all the students at Jesse's school told her they participate in a school club or sports team? For numbers 9a–9c, select the correct values to describe how to solve the problem.

9a. Draw a rectangular array with 3 rows and [3 / **(4)** / 5] columns.

9b. Shade [1 / **(2)** / 3] of the rows gray and [4 / 5 / **(6)**] of the gray squares black.

9c. Of all the students, [**($\frac{1}{2}$)** / $\frac{3}{4}$ / $\frac{3}{8}$] told Jesse they participate in a school club or sports team.

11. Write seventeen thousand and one hundred six thousandths in standard form.

17,000.106

GO ON

Name ____________________

11. It took Mary Lou $\frac{5}{6}$ hour to write a report for English class. It took Heather $\frac{9}{10}$ as much time to write her report as it took Mary Lou. Which statements are true? Mark all that apply.

- (A) Mary Lou and Heather take the same amount of time to write their reports.
- (B) ● Mary Lou spent more time writing her report than Heather.
- (C) ● Heather took $\frac{3}{4}$ hour to write her report.

12. Four friends share 3 apples equally. What fraction of an apple does each friend get?

Each friend will get $\frac{3}{4}$ of an apple.

13. Julia has 36 books. She wants to donate $\frac{2}{3}$ of them to a library book drive. How many books will she donate? Draw a model to show how you found your answer.

Possible answer:

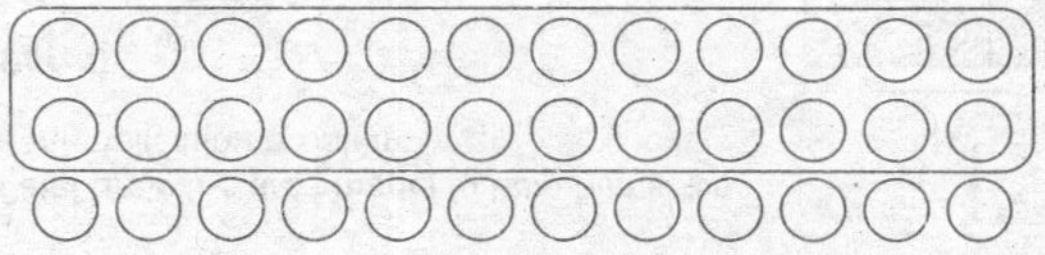

24 books

14. Multiply. Show your work.

$$\begin{array}{r} 385 \\ \times\ 32 \\ \hline \end{array}$$

12,320

Check students' work.

GO ON

Name ______________________

15. A shipping crate holds 22 boxes of pens. Each box measures 2 inches by 3 inches by 8 inches. Which statements are true? Mark all that apply.

- **(A)** Each box of pens has a volume of 48 cubic inches. (marked)
- (B) Each crate has a volume of about 960 cubic inches.
- (C) If the crate held 25 boxes of pens, it would have a volume of 550 cubic inches.
- **(D)** If the crate held 30 boxes of pens, it would have a volume of 1,440 cubic inches. (marked)

16. Myra is painting a 108-inch by 22-inch mural along the gym wall. How many square inches will she paint? Write the numbers in the boxes that will complete the model and then solve.

	20	+ 2
100	2,000	200
+ 8	160	16

2,376 square inches

17. 43.096 (<) > = 43.906

Name ______________________

18. Multiply. Draw a number line to show your work.

$2 \times \frac{1}{5} = \boxed{\frac{2}{5}}$

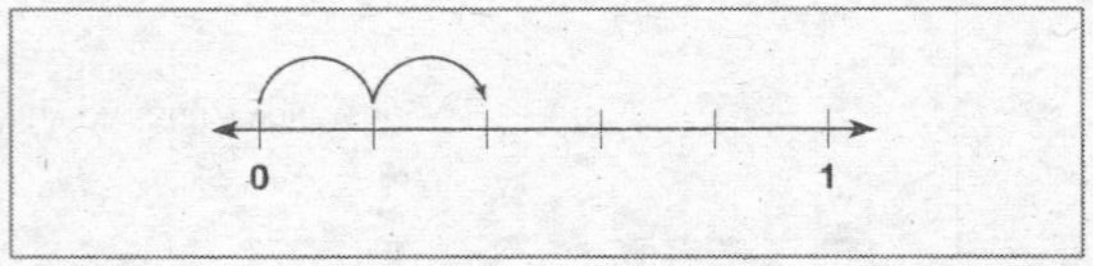

19. Patel drew the area model to help him solve a multiplication problem.

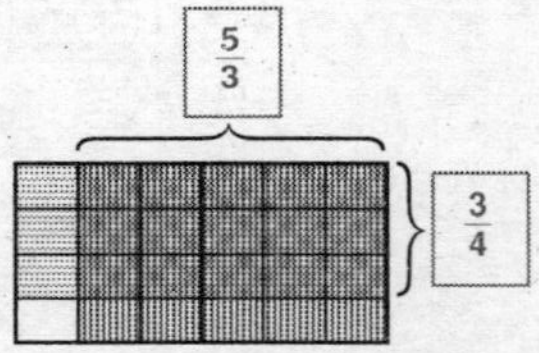

Part A

Use the numbers from the list on the right to complete the area model.

$\frac{4}{3}$ $\frac{5}{3}$ $\frac{3}{5}$ $\frac{3}{4}$

Part B

What is the answer to the problem Patel was working on? Show your work.

$\frac{5}{3} \times \frac{3}{4} = \frac{5}{\cancel{3}_1} \times \frac{\cancel{3}^1}{4} = \frac{5}{4} = 1\frac{1}{4}$

20. Write $\frac{5}{6}$ and $\frac{7}{9}$ as equivalent fractions that could be used to find the sum of the fractions.

Possible answers:

$\boxed{\frac{15}{18}}$ and $\boxed{\frac{14}{18}}$

21. Draw a rectangle to model the multiplication problem.

$2\frac{3}{5} \times 3\frac{7}{10}$

Check students' drawings.

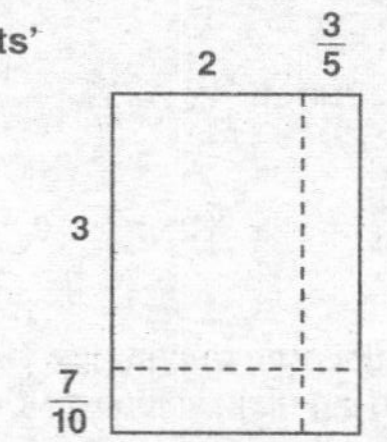

22. Joanne made a figure with cubes that measure 1 centimeter on each side. What is the volume of Joanne's figure?

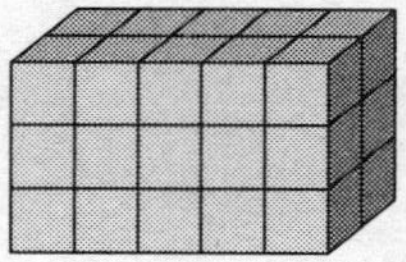

30 cubic centimeters

23. Match the figure with the number of unit cubes that would be needed to build each figure. Not every number of unit cubes will be used.

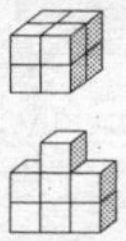

- 7 unit cubes
- 8 unit cubes
- 9 unit cubes
- 10 unit cubes

24. Aidan wants to make $\frac{1}{2}$ of a batch of muffins. The recipe calls for $\frac{2}{3}$ cup of milk for a whole batch. How much milk should Aiden use?

$\frac{2}{6}$ or $\frac{1}{3}$ cup

GO ON

25. Teresa has cubes that measure 3 inches on each side. Which of the statements are true? Mark all that apply.

- (A) ● The volume of one cube is 27 cubic inches.
- (B) If Teresa fills a box with 10 cubes, the volume of the box is about 200 cubic inches.
- (C) ● If the volume of the box is 810 cubic inches, Teresa can fit 30 cubes in the box.
- (D) If the volume of the box is 1,000 cubes, Teresa can fit 40 cubes in the box.

26. Jane used 1-centimeter cubes to build the rectangular prism shown. Find the volume of the rectangular prism Jane built.

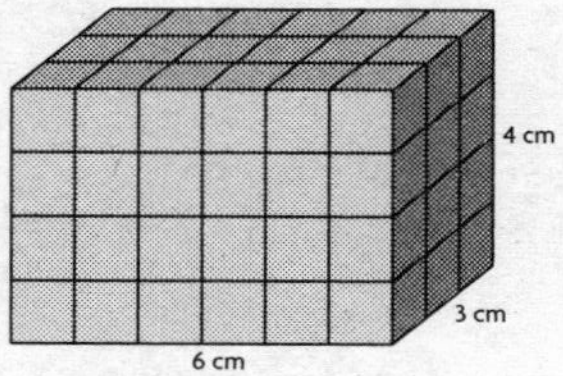

72 cubic centimeters

27. Alison used cubes to build this figure. What is the volume of the figure?

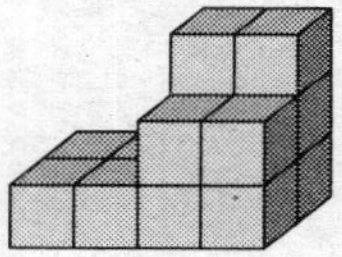

14 cubic units

28. Multiply. Show your work.

$$\begin{array}{r} 874 \\ \times\ 23 \\ \hline \boxed{20{,}102} \end{array}$$

GO ON

Alberto's Fish Tank

Alberto gets a fish-tank kit for his birthday. The kit comes with a 15-gallon tank, bags of colored gravel, and water-cleaning drops. Use this information to answer questions 1–4. Show your work. Write all answers in simplest form.

1. The chart below shows how much of each color of gravel Alberto puts in the bottom of his fish tank.

Color	Black	Gray	White	Yellow
Gravel (pounds)	$\frac{1}{4}$	$\frac{7}{8}$	$\frac{1}{2}$	$\frac{1}{8}$

a. How many pounds of gravel does Alberto put in the tank?

$\frac{1}{4} + \frac{7}{8} + \frac{1}{2} + \frac{1}{8} = \frac{2}{8} + \frac{7}{8} + \frac{4}{8} + \frac{1}{8} = \frac{14}{8} = 1\frac{6}{8} = 1\frac{3}{4}$

$1\frac{3}{4}$ pounds

b. Each color of gravel comes in an $8\frac{1}{2}$-pound bag. How many pounds of gravel will Alberto have left after he's put gravel in his tank?

Possible solution: $8\frac{1}{2} \times 4 = \frac{17}{2} \times 4 = \frac{68}{2} = 34$ total pounds of gravel

$34 - 1\frac{3}{4} = \frac{136}{4} - \frac{7}{4} = \frac{129}{4} = 32\frac{1}{4}$ pounds left

$32\frac{1}{4}$ pounds

GO ON

2. Once the gravel is in place, Alberto wants to fill his tank with water.

a. The gravel takes up the same space in the tank as about $\frac{1}{5}$ gallon of water. Alberto wants to leave an additional $\frac{1}{2}$ gallon of space in the tank for fish and plants. How much water does Alberto need to add to fill the 15-gallon tank?

$w + \frac{1}{5} + \frac{1}{2} = 15$

$w = 15 - \frac{1}{5} - \frac{1}{2}$

$w = 15 - \frac{2}{10} - \frac{5}{10}$

$w = \frac{150}{10} - \frac{7}{10}$

$w = \frac{143}{10} = 14\frac{3}{10}$

$14\frac{3}{10}$ gallons

b. Water evaporates at the rate of $\frac{1}{8}$ inch per hour. How much water will evaporate in 24 hours?

$24 \times \frac{1}{8} = \frac{24}{8} = 3$

3 inches

c. If each inch of water that evaporates is equal to $\frac{2}{25}$ gallon of water, how many gallons of water will evaporate in 24 hours?

$3 \times \frac{2}{25} = \frac{6}{25}$

$\frac{6}{25}$ gallon

GO ON

Name ______________________

Middle-of-Year Performance Task

3. Alberto puts 3 kinds of fish in his fish tank: zebra danios, fancy guppies, and catfish. Half of Alberto's fish are zebra danios. He has 2 times as many catfish as he has fancy guppies.

   a. Alberto's friend Jackson says that $\frac{1}{3}$ of Alberto's fish are catfish. Is Jackson correct? Draw a diagram and explain your answer.

Yes; Possible explanation: If $\frac{1}{2}$ of Alberto's fish are zebra danios, then the other $\frac{1}{2}$ are fancy guppies and catfish. I found that $\frac{1}{3}$ is 2 times as many as $\frac{1}{6}$. $\frac{1}{3} + \frac{1}{6} = \frac{2}{6} + \frac{1}{6} = \frac{3}{6} = \frac{1}{2}$.

Possible diagram shown.

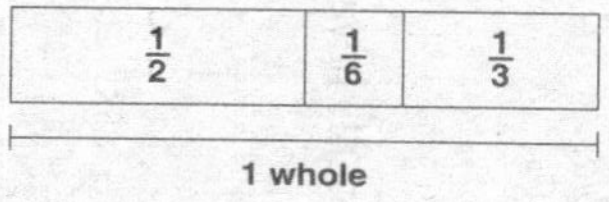

   b. One of Alberto's zebra danios is $\frac{4}{3}$ the length of one of his fancy guppies. Which fish is longer? Explain how you know.

The zebra danios is longer; Possible explanation: $\frac{4}{3}$ is a number greater than 1 whole. If you multiply a number by a number greater than 1, you will get a greater number than what you started with.

GO ON

Name ______________________

Middle-of-Year Performance Task

4. Alberto feeds his fish the same amount of food each day. He measures and finds the fish eat $\frac{1}{50}$ ounce of fish food per day.

   a. How many ounces of food will Alberto need for 110 days? Explain how you found your answer.

$2\frac{1}{5}$ ounces; Possible explanation: I multiplied $\frac{1}{50}$ by 110 days to find how much food is needed; $\frac{1}{50} \times 110 = \frac{110}{50}$ or $2\frac{1}{5}$.

   b. Alberto is thinking of buying a jar of fish food flakes that will last 110 days. If he does not change the number of fish, how many of these jars of fish food flakes would Alberto need to buy in 1 year?

$365 \times \frac{1}{110} = \frac{365}{110} = 7\frac{3}{22} = 3\frac{7}{22}$ jars

4 jars

STOP

Operations with Fractions

Alberto's Fish Tank

COMMON CORE STANDARDS

5.NF.A.1	Add and subtract fractions with unlike denominators (including mixed numbers) by replacing given fractions with equivalent fractions in such a way as to produce an equivalent sum or difference of fractions with like denominators.
5.NF.A.2	Solve word problems involving addition and subtraction of fractions referring to the same whole, including cases of unlike denominators, e.g., by using visual fraction models or equations to represent the problem.
5.NF.B.6	Solve real world problems involving multiplication of fractions and mixed numbers, e.g., by using visual fraction models or equations to represent the problem.
MP1	Make sense of problems and persevere in solving them.
MP7	Look for and make use of structure.

Also 5.NF.B.4a, MP2, MP3, MP4, MP5, MP6, MP8

PURPOSE

To assess the ability to represent and solve problems by writing and evaluating expressions with fractions

TIME

40–45 minutes

GROUPING

Individuals

MATERIALS

- Performance Task, paper, pencil

PREPARATION HINTS

- Review operations with fractions with students before assigning the task.
- Review vocabulary, including *simplest form*, *pattern*, and *rule*.

IMPLEMENTATION NOTES

- Read the task aloud to students and make sure that all students have a clear understanding of the task.
- Students may use manipulatives to complete the task.
- Allow students as much paper as they need to complete the task.
- Allow as much time as students need to complete the task.
- Students must complete the task individually, without collaboration.
- Collect all student work when the task is complete.

TASK SUMMARY

Students write and solve expressions involving operations with fractions.

REPRESENTATION

In this task teachers can...

- Activate prior knowledge by showing and discussing with students real-world videos related to the task.

ACTION and EXPRESSION

In this task teachers can...

- Build students' executive functioning skills by helping them set interim goals for completing each section of the task.

ENGAGEMENT

In this task, teachers can...

- Support students' efforts and persistence by allowing them to build individual, short breaks into their work schedules for the task.

EXPECTED STUDENT OUTCOMES

- Complete the task within the time allowed
- Reflect engagement in a productive struggle
- Apply operations with fractions to represent and solve word problems

SCORING

Use the associated Rubric to evaluate each student's work.

Performance Task Rubric

ALBERTO'S FISH TANK	
A level 3 response	• Shows the student has made sense of the task and persevered • Demonstrates ability to add, subtract, and multiply fractions • Shows ability to relate the sizes of factors to products • Demonstrates understanding of fractions as division
A level 2 response	• Shows the student has made sense of the task and persevered • Demonstrates ability to add, subtract, and multiply fractions • Shows ability to relate the sizes of factors to products • Demonstrates understanding of fractions as division • Addresses most or all aspects of the task, using mathematically sound procedures • May contain an incorrect answer derived from a correct procedure
A level 1 response	• Shows that the student has made sense of at least some components of the task • Shows uneven ability to perform operations with fractions • May show inability to relate sizes of factors to products • May show little understanding of fractions as division
A level 0 response	• Shows little evidence that the student has made sense of the task • Shows inability to perform operations with fractions • Shows little evidence of addressing the components of the task

Name ______________________

End-of-Year Test
Page 1

1. Fahed buys 12 stickers for $2 each. He also buys 4 sticker albums. Each album costs twice as much as each sticker. Fahed has a coupon that gives him $2 off the sticker albums. Which numerical expression shows how much he spent?

Ⓐ $(12 \times 2) + [(4 \times 2) - 2]$
● B $(12 \times 2) + [(4 \times 4) - 2]$
Ⓒ $(12 \times 4) + [(4 \times 4) - 2]$
Ⓓ $(12 \times 4) + [(4 \times 2) + 2]$

2. Select the number in which the digit 8 is ten times the value of the digit 8 in 4.381. Mark all that apply.

Ⓐ 183.9
Ⓑ 3.458
● C 56.82
Ⓓ 9.548
Ⓔ 0.184
● F 1.83

3. Rasheed needs to save $231. To earn money, he plans to wash cars and charge $12 per car. Write two estimates Rasheed could use to determine how many cars he needs to wash.

240 ÷ 12 = 20 and 230 ÷ 10 = 23

4. Casey is building a stage and a raised platform for the school play. The diagram below shows what Casey has built. What is the total volume of the stage and the platform?

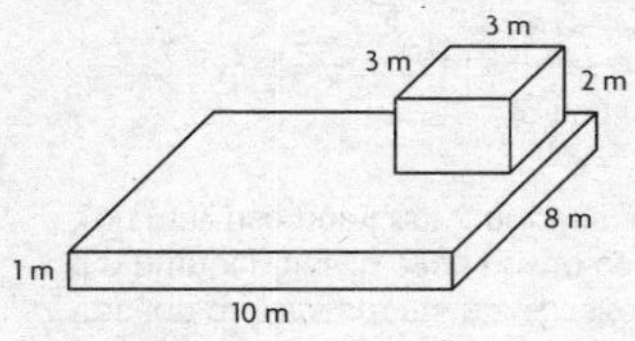

98 cubic meters

GO ON

Name ______________________

End-of-Year Test
Page 2

5. 1.143 [< / **(>)** / =] 0.485

6. Write two equivalent fractions that could be used to solve $\frac{2}{3} + \frac{3}{4}$. Use a common denominator. **Possible answers:**

$\frac{8}{12}$ and $\frac{9}{12}$

7. Use the numbers on the tiles to write the value of each expression. You can use a tile more than once or not at all.

$48.6 \div 10^0$ = **48.6**

$48.6 \div 10$ = **4.86**

$48.6 \div 10^2$ = **0.486**

Tiles: . | 0 | 4 | 6 | 8

8. Samuel walked in the Labor Day parade. He walked $3\frac{1}{4}$ miles along the parade route and $2\frac{5}{6}$ miles home. For numbers 8a–8c, fill in each blank.

8a. Rounded to the closest benchmark, Samuel walked about **3** miles on the parade route.

8b. Rounded to the closest benchmark, Samuel walked about **3** miles home.

8c. Samuel walked about **6** miles in all.

GO ON

9. Mr. Enders conducted a survey and found that $\frac{2}{5}$ of his students play a team sport and $\frac{1}{4}$ of those students play basketball. What fraction of his students play basketball? Write a number from the number tiles in each box to complete the calculations shown. You may use numbers more than once or not at all.

$\frac{2}{5} \times \frac{1}{4} = \frac{2 \times \boxed{1}}{5 \times \boxed{4}} = \frac{\boxed{2}}{\boxed{20}} = \frac{\boxed{1}}{\boxed{10}}$

Tiles: 1, 2, 3, 4, 5, 10, 12, 20

$\frac{1}{10}$ of his students

10. Write 6.847 in word form.

six and eight hundred forty-seven thousandths

11. For numbers 11a–11d, without multiplying, use the symbols from the list on the right to indicate how the product will compare with the factor. Symbols can be used more than once.

11a. $\frac{3}{4} \times \frac{15}{7} = x$ — x [>] $\frac{3}{4}$ — x [<] $\frac{15}{7}$

11b. $7 \times \frac{6}{5} = x$ — x [>] 7 — x [>] $\frac{6}{5}$

11c. $\frac{8}{9} \times \frac{1}{5} = x$ — x [<] $\frac{8}{9}$ — x [<] $\frac{1}{5}$

11d. $\frac{8}{8} \times \frac{7}{10} = x$ — x [<] $\frac{8}{8}$ — x [=] $\frac{7}{10}$

Tiles: <, >, =

GO ON

12. Twelve friends share 4 bread rolls equally. What fraction of a bread roll does each friend get?

Each friend will get $\frac{4}{12}$ or $\frac{1}{3}$ of a bread roll.

13. For numbers 13a–13c, write the name of one figure from the tiles to complete a true statement. Use each figure only once.

13a. A [pentagon] is never a parallelogram.

13b. A [parallelogram] is sometimes a rhombus.

13c. A [square] is always a rectangle.

Tiles: pentagon, parallelogram, square

14. Megan wants to find the quotient. Use multiplication and the Distributive Property to help Megan find the quotient.

$72 \div 4 = \boxed{18}$

Multiplication: $18 \times 4 = 72$

Distributive Property: $(4 \times 10) + (4 \times 8)$

15. Describe how to locate the ordered pair (6, 8) on a coordinate plane. Begin your description at the origin.

Possible description: From the origin, move 6 units to the right along the x-axis. Then move 8 units up.

GO ON

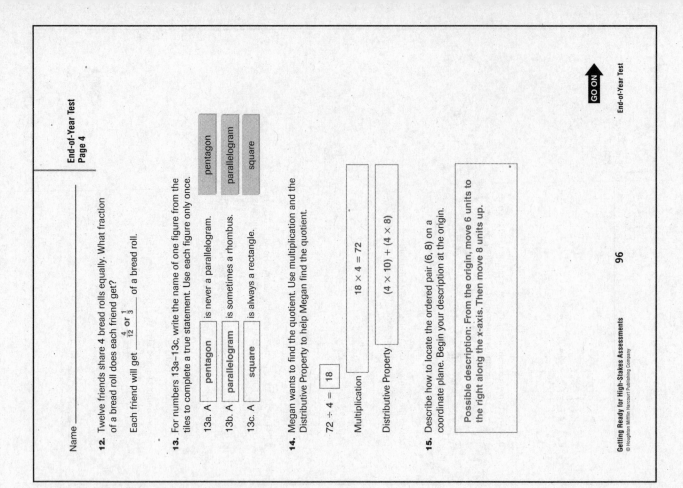

16. Multiply 7,952 × 836. Explain how you know your answer is reasonable.

6,647,872; Possible explanation: 7,952 rounds to 8,000 and 836 rounds to 800. To estimate the product I found 8,000 × 800 = 6,400,000. This is close to the answer I calculated, so my answer is reasonable.

17. Write the letter for the place value in the box next to the number that shows 143.649 rounded to that place value.

A tenths	E	143.65
B hundreds	B	100
C ones	C	144
D tens	A	143.6
E hundredths	D	140

18. Choose the numbers to create a story problem that represents $\frac{1}{2} \div 3$.

Rob bought [$\frac{1}{3}$ / ($\frac{1}{2}$) / 3] pound(s) of roast beef.

He made 3 sandwiches for a picnic and used the same amount of roast beef in each sandwich.

Rob used [$\frac{2}{3}$ / ($\frac{1}{6}$) / 6] pound(s) of roast beef in each sandwich.

GO ON

19. Rahul draws the area model to help him solve a multiplication problem.

Part A

Use the numbers from the list on the right to complete the area model.

$\frac{3}{2}$

$\frac{7}{5}$

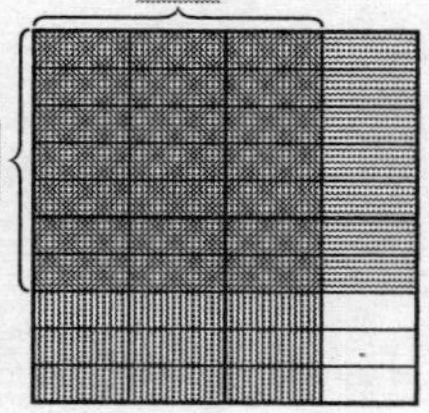

$\frac{5}{7}$ $\frac{7}{5}$ $\frac{3}{2}$ $\frac{2}{3}$

Part B

What is the answer to the problem Rahul was working on? Show your work.

$\frac{7}{5} \times \frac{3}{2} = \frac{21}{10} = 2\frac{1}{10}$

20. Karl drove 617.3 miles. For each gallon of gas, the car can travel 41 miles. Select a reasonable estimate of the number of gallons of gas Karl used. Mark all that apply.

- (A) 1.5 gallons
- (B) 1.6 gallons
- (C) 15 gallons ●
- (D) 16 gallons ●
- (E) 150 gallons

GO ON

Name ______________________

21. Without multiplying, classify each product as being less than $\frac{5}{6}$, equal to $\frac{5}{6}$, or greater than $\frac{5}{6}$. Write the letter of each expression in the correct box.

A $\frac{5}{6} \times \frac{4}{1}$ **B** $\frac{5}{6} \times \frac{3}{4}$ **C** $\frac{5}{6} \times \frac{1}{4}$ **D** $\frac{5}{6} \times \frac{3}{3}$ **E** $\frac{5}{6} \times \frac{3}{5}$ **F** $\frac{5}{6} \times \frac{5}{1}$

Less Than $\frac{5}{6}$	Equal to $\frac{5}{6}$	Greater Than $\frac{5}{6}$
B, C, E	**D**	**A, F**

22. Shane filled bags with pebbles. The weights of the bags are $\frac{1}{6}$ lb, $\frac{1}{3}$ lb, $\frac{2}{3}$ lb, $\frac{1}{3}$ lb, $\frac{1}{2}$ lb, $\frac{1}{6}$ lb, $\frac{1}{6}$ lb, $\frac{1}{3}$ lb, $\frac{2}{3}$ lb, $\frac{1}{2}$ lb, $\frac{1}{3}$ lb, $\frac{1}{6}$ lb, $\frac{1}{6}$ lb, $\frac{1}{6}$ lb, $\frac{1}{3}$ lb, $\frac{1}{3}$ lb. Organize the information in a line plot.

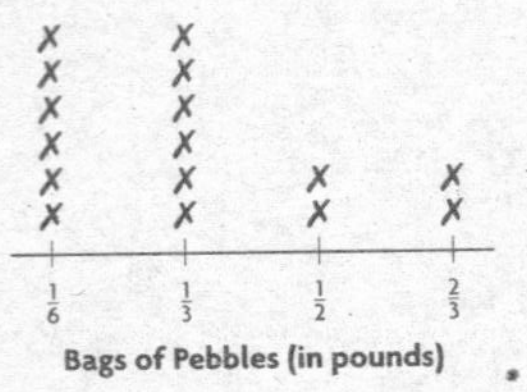

What is the average weight of the bags?

$\frac{1}{3}$ pound(s)

23. Match the figure with the number of unit cubes that would be needed to build each figure. Not every number of unit cubes will be used.

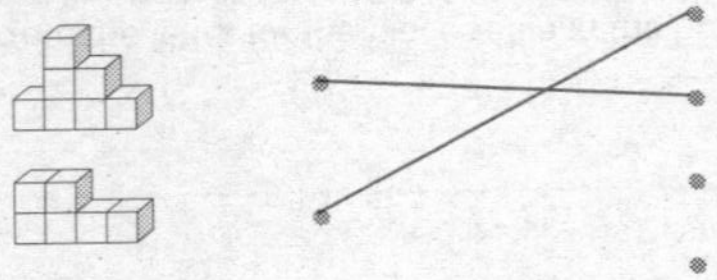

6 unit cubes

7 unit cubes

8 unit cubes

9 unit cubes

24. Ava has two frogs. This is $\frac{1}{3}$ the number of frogs that Heather has. How many frogs does Heather have? Draw a diagram to represent the division. Then write and solve an equation.

6 frogs; Equations may vary. Possible equation: $x = 2 \div \frac{1}{3}$; Check students' drawings.

GO ON

Name ______________________

25. Jake has cubes that measure 5 inches on each side. Which of the statements are true? Mark all that apply.

Ⓐ The volume of one cube is 25 cubic inches.

● **B** If Jake fills a box with 12 cubes, the volume of the box is about 1,500 cubic inches.

● **C** If the volume of the box is 800 cubic inches, Jake can fit 6 cubes in the box.

Ⓓ If the volume of the box is 1,000 cubes, Jake can fit 10 cubes in the box.

26. Raul used 1-centimeter cubes to build the rectangular prism shown. Find the volume of the rectangular prism Raul built.

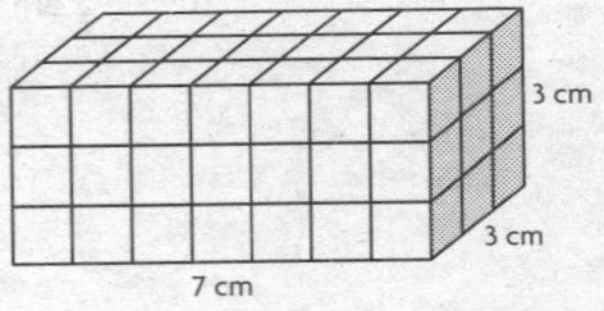

63 cubic centimeters

27. Clarice packed 1-inch cubes into a box with a volume of 36 cubic inches. How many layers of 1-inch cubes did Clarice pack?

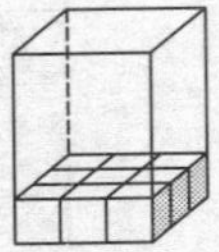

4 layers

28. Kristin drew a triangle with 2 congruent sides and 1 right angle. Which term accurately describes the triangle? Mark all that apply.

● **A** isosceles ● **C** right

Ⓑ scalene Ⓓ obtuse

GO ON

Name ____________________

End-of-Year Performance Task

Water Rush

1. Ms. Luca designs a new water ride for a theme park. The coordinate grid shows her plan for the path of the boats through the ride.

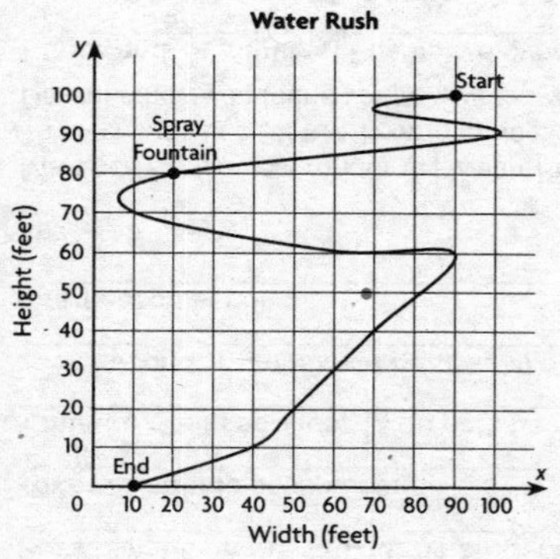

a. What are the coordinates of the Start and End of the ride?

Start: (90, 100); End: (10, 0)

b. Ms. Luca decides to place a waterfall 50 feet to the right and 30 feet below the Spray Fountain. What ordered pair describes the location of the waterfall?

(70, 50)

c. Plot and label the location of the waterfall on the coordinate grid above.

GO ON

Name ____________________

End-of-Year Performance Task

2. Once the Water Rush ride is built, Ms. Luca begins safety tests. For every 10 tests she runs, Ms. Luca finds and fixes 15 safety errors. Fill in the missing numbers in the table.

Tests Run	10	20	30	40	50
Errors Fixed	15	30	45	60	75

a. What rule could you write that relates Tests Run to Errors Fixed?

Possible rule: Divide the number of Tests Run by 10, and then multiply by 15.

b. Graph Ms. Luca's data.

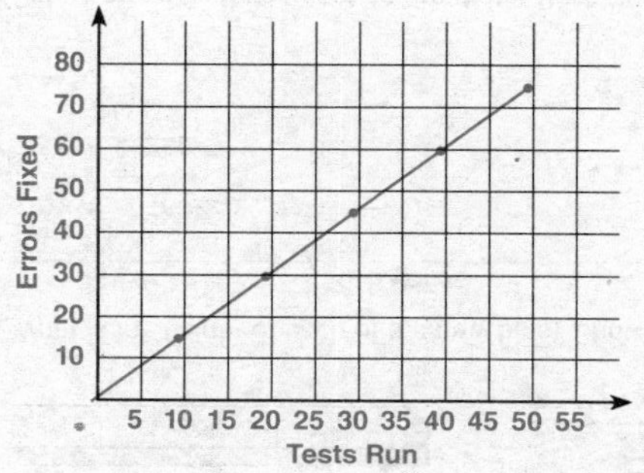

c. Estimate the number of errors Ms. Luca could expect to find and fix if she runs 33 tests. Explain how you found your answer.

Possible estimate: 50 errors; I know my answer will be between 45 errors for 30 tests run and 60 errors for 40 tests run. I found 33 tests run on the x-axis and drew a line to where 33 tests would hit the line on the graph. It's about where the line crosses 50 on the y-axis.

GO ON

3. Boats going through the Water Rush ride travel 0.06 mile. The most popular ride in the theme park is 174 yards long. What is the difference between the length of this ride and the length of Water Rush in feet? Show your work.

205.2 feet

0.06 mile × 5,280 feet = 316.8 feet

174 yards × 3 feet = 522 feet

522 − 316.8 = 205.2 feet

4. Plans say that 1,800 gallons of water are recycled through the Water Rush ride each minute. Ms. Luca wants to make a statement about the number of quarts of water that are recycled each second. What should her statement be? Show your work.

Possible statement: 120 quarts are recycled through the Water Rush ride each second.

1 minute = 60 seconds; 1,800 gallons ÷ 60 = 30 gallons each second; 1 gallon = 4 quarts; 30 gallons × 4 = 120 quarts each second

5. Ms. Luca starts a test run for the Water Rush ride at 3:58 P.M. The test ends at 5:22 P.M. How long does the test last? Describe how you found your answer.

1 hour and 24 minutes; Possible explanation: I started by subtracting 1 hour from 5:22 to get 4:22. Then I subtracted 22 minutes to get to 4:00. I subtracted 2 more minutes to get to 3:58, which means that the test lasts 1 hour and 24 minutes.

GO ON

6. In her first design for Water Rush, Ms. Luca used 4 same-size rectangular bins to hold sand. Each bin had a volume of 180 cubic yards. Then Ms. Luca changed her design to use 2 new same-size rectangular bins. The total volume of the 2 new bins is equivalent to the total volume of the 4 original bins.

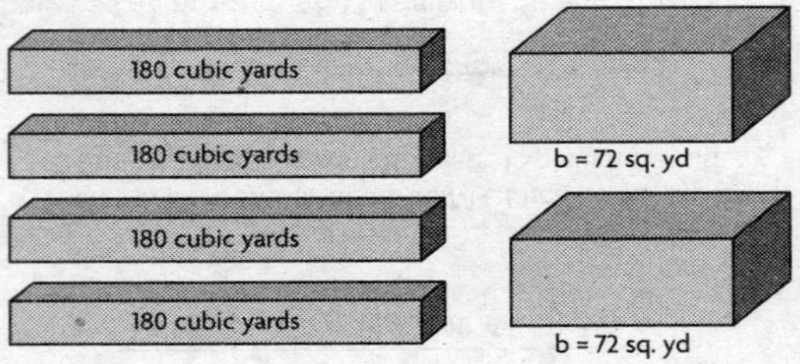

What is the height of each of the new bins? Show your work.

5 yards

$72 \times h = 180 \times 2$

$72 \times h = 360$

$h = 5$

7. Riders go up 2 steps to get on the Water Rush boats. The drawing shows the measurements of the steps.

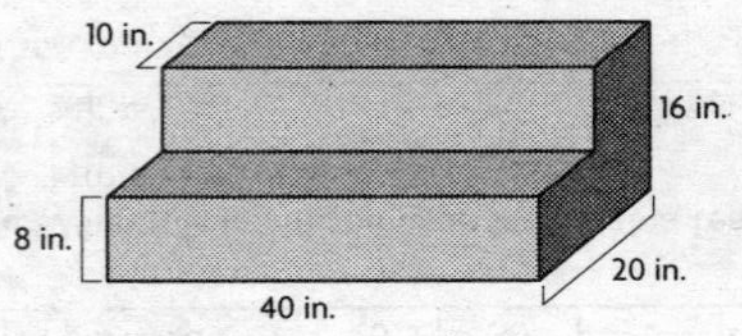

20 in. × 40 in. × 8 in. = 6,400

10 in. × 40 in. × 8 in. = 3,200

6,400 + 3,200 = 9,600 cubic inches

What is the total volume of the steps? Show your work.

9,600 cubic inches

STOP

Geometry and Measurement

Water Rush

COMMON CORE STANDARDS

5.G.A.2 Represent real world and mathematical problems by graphing points in the first quadrant of the coordinate plane, and interpret coordinate values of points in the context of the situation.

5.MD.A.1 Convert among different-sized standard measurement units within a given measurement system, and use these conversions in solving multi-step real world problems.

5.MD.C.5b. Apply the formulas $V = l \times w \times h$ and $V = B \times h$ for rectangular prisms to find volumes of right rectangular prisms with whole-number edge lengths in the context of solving real world and mathematical problems.

MP1 Make sense of problems and persevere in solving them.

Also 5.OA.B.3, MP4, MP6, MP7

PURPOSE

To assess the ability to represent and solve problems by graphing and analyzing data, by converting measurements within the customary and metric systems, and by calculating volume of rectangular prisms

TIME

40–45 minutes

GROUPING

Individuals

MATERIALS

- Performance Task, paper, pencil

PREPARATION HINTS

- Review operations with whole numbers, fractions, and decimals with students before assigning the task.
- Review vocabulary, including *coordinate grid*, *ordered pair*, *estimate*, *volume*, and the customary and metric units of measurement.

IMPLEMENTATION NOTES

- Read the task aloud to students and make sure that all students have a clear understanding of the task.
- Students may use manipulatives to complete the task.
- Allow students as much paper as they need to complete the task.
- Allow as much time as students need to complete the task.
- Students must complete the task individually, without collaboration.
- Collect all student work when the task is complete.

TASK SUMMARY

Students solve problems involving graphing and analyzing data, converting among units of measurement, and finding volume of rectangular prisms.

REPRESENTATION

In this task teachers can…

- Help students activate learning from the previous chapters by reviewing relevant content using student volunteers.

ACTION and EXPRESSION

In this task teachers can…

- Provide graduated levels of support to build fluency by modeling how to break down similar problems into intermediate steps prior to assigning the task, and encouraging struggling students to take things one step at a time while completing the task.

ENGAGEMENT

In this task, teachers can…

- Optimize relevance and recruit interest by discussing student's own personal experiences relevant to the task.
- Support students' efforts and persistence by offering feedback that recognizes perseverance and improvement.

EXPECTED STUDENT OUTCOMES

- Complete the task within the time allowed
- Reflect engagement in a productive struggle
- Graph and analyze data, convert among units of measurement, and find volume of rectangular prisms to represent and solve word problems

SCORING

Use the associated Rubric to evaluate each student's work.

Performance Task Rubric

WATER RUSH	
A level 3 response	• Shows the student has made sense of the task and persevered • Shows ability to use coordinate grids and relationships between numerical patterns • Shows ability to find elapsed time and compare and convert among measurement units • Demonstrates understanding of volume and applies volume formula
A level 2 response	• Shows the student has made sense of the task and persevered • Shows ability to use coordinate grids and relationships between numerical patterns • Shows ability to find elapsed time and compare and convert among measurement units • Demonstrates understanding of volume and applies volume formula • Addresses most or all aspects of the task • May contain an incorrect answer derived from a correct procedure
A level 1 response	• Shows the student has made sense of some components of the task • May show uneven ability to convert within measurement systems or apply volume concepts • May show difficulty describing or extending a relationship between two numerical sequences
A level 0 response	• Shows little evidence that the student has made sense of the task • Shows inability to convert within measurement systems, to apply volume concepts, or to describe or extend a numerical relationship • Shows little evidence of addressing the components of the task

Joanna's Healthy Treats

Joanna owns and runs a bakery that makes healthy snacks. She has many great treats in her shop, but her most popular snacks are muffins, homemade granola bars, and bags of healthy snack mix. She makes several batches of these each day. In order to make her snacks, Joanna has the ingredients shipped to her bakery in bulk. She then uses recipes to make sure she gets the amount of each ingredient exactly right for each treat.

One of Joanna's best-loved treats are her oatmeal blueberry muffins. In order to make one batch, she needs these ingredients:

$\frac{2}{3}$ cup oats

$\frac{5}{6}$ cup flour

$\frac{3}{4}$ cup of sugar

1 teaspoon baking powder

1 teaspoon baking soda

$\frac{3}{4}$ teaspoon salt

$\frac{1}{2}$ cup milk

2 eggs

2 cups of blueberries

GO ON

Joanna always uses fresh ingredients. Each day, the bakery gets shipments of ingredients like flour, milk, eggs, fruit, and oats for Joanna's recipes. The ingredients often come in large crates. This is so that she has enough ingredients to make enough of each treat for her customers.

Some of the bulk packages Joanna receives each day include dried fruit to use in her granola bars and snack mix.

Boxes of raisins come in a crate like the one shown.

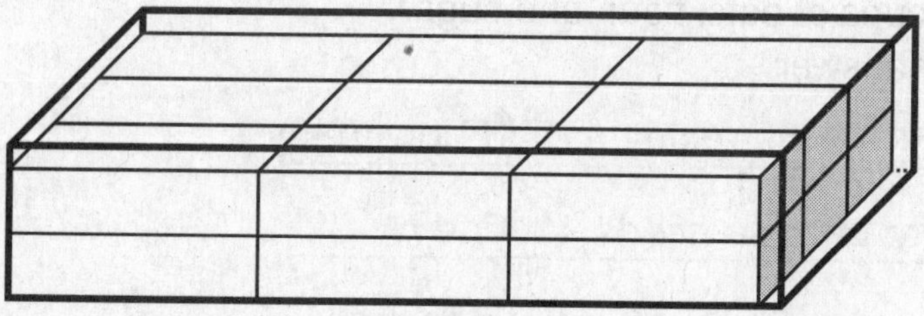

Each 20-ounce box of raisins measures 6 inches wide by 8 inches tall by 2 inches deep.

Dried cranberries come in crates like the one shown.

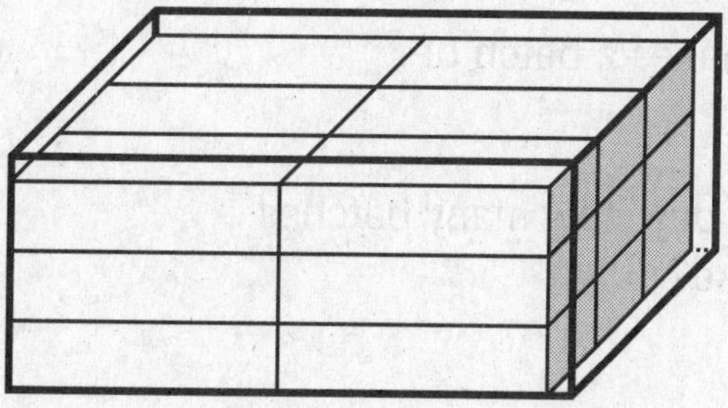

Each 8-ounce box of dried cranberries measures 4 inches wide by 6 inches tall by 3 inches deep.

GO ON

Use the recipe on page 105 to answer questions 1–4. Show your work.

1. How many cups of oats, flour, and sugar does Joanna need for this recipe?

$\frac{2}{3} + \frac{5}{6} + \frac{3}{4} = \frac{8}{12} + \frac{10}{12} + \frac{9}{12} = \frac{27}{12} = 2\frac{3}{12} = 2\frac{1}{4}$

Joanna needs $2\frac{1}{4}$ cups of oats, flour, and sugar.
Describe how you found your answer.

Possible description: I looked at the recipe to find how many cups of flour, oats, and sugar Joanna needs. I found a common denominator for the fractions. After I added the fractions with the common denominator, I used division to change the sum into a mixed number.

2. The oatmeal blueberry muffin recipe makes a batch of 16 muffins.

a. If the bakery sells 144 muffins each day, how many batches of muffins does Joanna need to make?

$144 \div 16 = 9$

Joanna needs to make 9 batches.

b. How many cups of flour does Joanna need to make 144 muffins?

$\frac{5}{6} \times 9 = \frac{5}{6} \times \frac{9}{1} = \frac{45}{6} = 7\frac{3}{6} = 7\frac{1}{2}$

Joanna needs $7\frac{1}{2}$ cups of flour.

GO ON

Name ____________________

3. The flour Joanna buys comes in 5-pound bags. One cup of flour weighs about $\frac{3}{10}$ pound. How many cups are in each bag of flour? Show your work.

$$5 \div \frac{3}{10} = \frac{5}{1} \times \frac{10}{3} = \frac{50}{3} = 16\frac{2}{3}$$

There are $16\frac{2}{3}$ cups of flour in each 5-pound bag.

4. Joanna sells one muffin for $0.55.

a. Mrs. Ramirez orders 36 muffins for a party. What will the cost of 36 muffins be?

0.55 × 36 = 19.80

36 muffins will cost a total of $ **19.80**.

b. After 4 P.M., Joanna offers a $0.25 discount on all of her baked goods. If Mrs. Ramirez orders her muffins after 4 P.M., what will the cost be?

0.55 − 0.25 = 0.30

0.30 × 36 = 10.80

36 muffins will cost a total of $ **10.80**.

c. How much money does Mrs. Ramirez save if she orders the muffins after 4 P.M.? Explain how you found your answer.

Mrs. Ramirez saves $9. Possible explanation:

I subtracted the cost of the muffins after 4 P.M. from the cost of the muffins before 4 P.M.; $19.80 − $10.80 = $9.00

GO ON

5. Joanna also uses oats in her granola bars.

a. Oats come in 42-ounce cans. Joanna uses 134.4 ounces of oats each day. How many cans of oats does Joanna need to order for one day?

134.4 ÷ 42 = 3.2

Joanna needs **4** cans of oats.

b. One week, Joanna gets a better deal on oats that come in packs of 2 cans that each contain 38.4 ounces. How many of these packs does she need in one day?

38.4 × 2 = 76.8

134.4 ÷ 76.8 = 1.75

Joanna needs **2** packs of oats.

6. Joanna puts almonds in some of her granola bars. Each 16-ounce bag contains 384 almonds. How many almonds are in 1 ounce? Show your work.

384 ÷ 16 = 24

There are **24** almonds in 1 ounce.

7. Joanna did a special promotion in July. Each customer will get a bag of snack mix containing oats, nuts, and small cookies. Each bag weighs 226 grams. There were 1,734 customers in July. How many grams of snack mix did Joanna need to make to give 1 bag to each customer? Show your work.

1,734 × 226 = 391,884

Joanna needs to make **391,884** grams of snack mix.

GO ON

Use the information about raisins and dried cranberries on page 106 to answer questions 7–8. Show your work.

8. Each 20-ounce box of raisins is 6 inches wide by 8 inches tall by 2 inches deep.

a. What is the volume of one box of raisins? Use the formula $V = l \times w \times h$ to find your answer.

6 × 8 × 2 = 96

The volume of one box of raisins is **96** cubic inches.

b. Look at the diagram of the crate on p. 106. Based on what you know about the volume of one box of raisins, what is the best estimate for the volume of the crate?

96 × 18 = 1,728

The volume of the crate is about **1,728** cubic inches.

c. If the crate itself weighs 6 ounces, what is the best estimate for the total weight of the crate?

(20 × 18) + 6 = 360 + 6 = 366

The crate weighs about **366** ounces.

9. What is the best estimate for the volume of the crate of dried cranberries? Explain how you know.

1,296 cubic inches; Possible explanation: Each box of dried cranberries is 4 inches wide by 6 inches tall by 3 inches deep, so the volume of one box is 72 cubic inches. The diagram shows 18 boxes in each crate. 72 cubic inches × 18 boxes = 1,296 cubic inches

STOP

Joanna's Healthy Treats

COMMON CORE STANDARDS

5.NBT.B.5	Fluently multiply multi-digit whole numbers using the standard algorithm.
5.NBT.B.6	Find whole-number quotients of whole numbers with up to four-digit dividends and two-digit divisors, using strategies based on place value, the properties of operations, and/or the relationship between multiplication and division. Illustrate and explain the calculation by using equations, rectangular arrays, and/or area models.
5.NBT.B.7	Add, subtract, multiply, and divide decimals to hundredths, using concrete models or drawings and strategies based on place value, properties of operations, and/or the relationship between addition and subtraction; relate the strategy to a written method and explain the reasoning used.
5.NF.A.1	Add and subtract fractions with unlike denominators (including mixed numbers) by replacing given fractions with equivalent fractions in such a way as to produce an equivalent sum or difference of fractions with like denominators.
5.NF.B.4a	Interpret the product $(a/b) \times q$ as a parts of a partition of q into b equal parts; equivalently, as the result of a sequence of operations $a \times q \div b$.
5.NF.B.7c	Solve real world problems involving division of unit fractions by non-zero whole numbers and division of whole numbers by unit fractions, e.g., by using visual fraction models and equations to represent the problem. For example, how much chocolate will each person get if 3 people share 1/2 lb of chocolate equally? How many 1/3-cup servings are in 2 cups of raisins?
5.MD.C.4	Measure volumes by counting unit cubes, using cubic cm, cubic in, cubic ft, and improvised units.
5.MD.C.5a	Find the volume of a right rectangular prism with whole-number side lengths by packing it with unit cubes, and show that the volume is the same as would be found by multiplying the edge lengths, equivalently by multiplying the height by the area of the base. Represent threefold whole-number products as volumes, e.g., to represent the associative property of multiplication.
5.MD.C.5b	Apply the formulas $V = l \times w \times h$ and $V = b \times h$ for rectangular prisms to find volumes of right rectangular prisms with whole-number edge lengths in the context of solving real world and mathematical problems.
MP1	Make sense of problems and persevere in solving them.

PURPOSE

To assess the ability to add and subtract fractions with unlike denominators, to multiply and divide fractions, to perform operations with multi-digit numbers, including decimals, and to find the volume of a rectangular prism.

TIME

40–45 minutes

GROUPING

Individuals

MATERIALS

- Performance Assessment Task, paper, pencil

PREPARATION HINTS

- Review operations with fractions and decimals and volume of a rectangular prism before assigning the task.
- Review vocabulary, including *volume*, *rectangular prism*

IMPLEMENTATION NOTES

- Read the task aloud to students and make sure that all students have a clear understanding of the task.
- Students may use manipulatives to complete the task.
- Allow students as much paper as they need to complete the task.
- Allow as much time as students need to complete the task.
- Students must complete the task individually, without collaboration.
- Collect all student work when the task is complete.

TASK SUMMARY

Students solve multi-step problems involving volume and operations with fractions, decimals, and multi-digit number.

REPRESENTATION

In this task teachers can…

- Activate prior knowledge by reviewing concepts and discussing the scenario.
- Guide children to visualize problems by picturing scenarios in their minds.

ACTION and EXPRESSION

In this task teachers can…

- Support strategy development by encouraging children to formulate a plan for solving.
- Support students' executive functioning by creating and displaying a schedule for working through the task.

ENGAGEMENT

In this task, teachers can…

- Provide options for self-assessment by offering strategies for checking work.
- Reduce distractions by involving students in whole class discussions of the task.

EXPECTED STUDENT OUTCOMES

- Complete the task within the time allowed.
- Reflect engagement in a productive struggle.
- Understand how to add and subtract fractions with unlike denominators.
- Understand how to perform operations and solve word problems with fractions.
- Understand and solve multi-step problems with multi-digit numbers and decimals.
- Recognize attributes and find the volume of rectangular prisms.

SCORING

Use the associated Rubric to evaluate each student's work.

Year-End Performance Assessment Task Rubric

JOANNA'S HEALTHY TREATS	
A level 3 response	• Indicates that the student has made sense of the task and persevered • Demonstrates an understanding of adding fractions with unlike denominators and of multiplying and dividing fractions • Shows an ability to add, subtract, multiply, and divide multi-digit numbers, including decimals • Indicates an understanding of how to find the volume of a rectangular prism
A level 2 response	• Indicates that the student has made sense of the task and persevered • Demonstrates an understanding of adding fractions with unlike denominators and of multiplying and dividing fractions • Shows an ability to add, subtract, multiply, and divide multi-digit numbers, including decimals • Indicates an understanding of how to find the volume of a rectangular prism • Addresses most or all aspects of the task, but there may be errors of omission
A level 1 response	• Shows that the student has made sense of at least some elements of the task • Shows some ability to add fractions with unlike denominators and to multiply and divide fractions • Demonstrates some understanding of how to add, subtract, multiply, and divide multi-digit numbers, including decimals • May not show understanding of how to find the volume of a rectangular prism
A level 0 response	• Shows little evidence that the student has made sense of the problems in the task • Shows an inability to add fractions with unlike denominators and to multiply and divide fractions • Shows an inability to add, subtract, multiply, and divide multi-digit numbers • Shows an inability to find the volume of rectangular prisms • Shows little evidence of addressing the elements of the task

Intervention Resources

		Personal Math Trainer	Response to Intervention
Domain: Operations and Algebraic Thinking			
Write and interpret numerical expressions.			
5.OA.A.1	Use parentheses, brackets, or braces in numerical expressions, and evaluate expressions with these symbols.	**5.OA.A.1**	Tier 1 Lessons: 1, 2 Tier 2/3 Skills and Activities: 13, 17, 27, 43, 48
5.OA.A.2	Write simple expressions that record calculations with numbers, and interpret numerical expressions without evaluating them.	**5.OA.A.2**	Tier 1 Lesson: 3 Tier 2/3 Skills and Activities: 9, 15, 19, 34
Analyze patterns and relationships.			
5.OA.B.3	Generate two numerical patterns using two given rules. Identify apparent relationships between corresponding terms. Form ordered pairs consisting of corresponding terms from the two patterns, and graph the ordered pairs on a coordinate plane.	**5.OA.B.3**	Tier 1 Lessons: 4, 5, 6 Tier 2/3 Skills and Activities: 23, 27, 33, 43, 46, 47, 64, 113
Domain: Number and Operations in Base Ten			
Understand the place value system.			
5.NBT.A.1	Recognize that in a multi-digit number, a digit in one place represents 10 times as much as it represents in the place to its right and 1/10 of what it represents in the place to its left.	**5.NBT.A.1**	Tier 1 Lessons: 7, 8, 9 Tier 2/3 Skills and Activities: 1, 2, 3, 4, 5, 23, 31, 71
5.NBT.A.2	Explain patterns in the number of zeros of the product when multiplying a number by powers of 10, and explain patterns in the placement of the decimal point when a decimal is multiplied or divided by a power of 10. Use whole-number exponents to denote powers of 10.	**5.NBT.A.2**	Tier 1 Lessons: 10, 11, 12, 13 Tier 2/3 Skills and Activities: 1, 6, 28, 29, 31, 39, 74
5.NBT.A.3	Read, write, and compare decimals to thousandths.	**5.NBT.A.3**	
5.NBT.A.3a	Read and write decimals to thousandths using base-ten numerals, number names, and expanded form, e.g., $347.392 = 3 \times 100 + 4 \times 10 + 7 \times 1 + 3 \times (1/10) + 9 \times (1/100) + 2 \times (1/1000)$.	**5.NBT.A.3a**	Tier 1 Lesson: 4 Tier 2/3 Skills and Activities: 2, 3, 71, 73
5.NBT.A.3b	Compare two decimals to thousandths based on meanings of the digits in each place, using >, =, and < symbols to record the results of comparisons.	**5.NBT.A.3b**	Tier 1 Lesson: 15 Tier 2/3 Skills and Activities: 74, 75
5.NBT.A.4	Use place value understanding to round decimals to any place.	**5.NBT.A.4**	Tier 1 Lesson: 16 Tier 2/3 Skills and Activities: 8, 74
Perform operations with multi-digit whole numbers and with decimals to hundredths.			
5.NBT.B.5	Fluently multiply multi-digit whole numbers using the standard algorithm.	**5.NBT.B.5**	Tier 1 Lessons: 17, 18 Tier 2/3 Skills and Activities: 2, 4, 14, 21, 25, 27, 30

Intervention Resources

		Personal Math Trainer	Response to Intervention
5.NBT.B.6	Find whole-number quotients of whole numbers with up to four-digit dividends and two-digit divisors, using strategies based on place value, the properties of operations, and/or the relationship between multiplication and division. Illustrate and explain the calculation by using equations, rectangular arrays, and/or area models.	**5.NBT.B.6**	Tier 1 Lessons: 19, 20, 21, 22, 23, 24, 25, 26, 27, 28, 29 Tier 2/3 Skills and Activities: 2, 5, 11, 13, 18, 20, 21, 22, 23, 28, 29, 31, 35, 36, 37, 39, 40, 41, 42, 43, 44, 45, 49
5.NBT.B.7	Add, subtract, multiply, and divide decimals to hundredths, using concrete models or drawings and strategies based on place value, properties of operations, and/or the relationship between addition and subtraction; relate the strategy to a written method and explain the reasoning used.	**5.NBT.B.7**	Tier 1 Lessons: 30, 31, 32, 33, 34, 35, 36, 37, 38, 39, 40, 41, 42, 43, 44, 45, 46, 47, 48, 49, 50, 51 Tier 2/3 Skills and Activities: 6, 8, 10, 12, 14, 16, 18, 19, 23, 26, 28, 32, 33, 34, 39, 42, 44, 45, 46, 71, 72, 73, 76, 77, 78, 79, 80, 81, 82, 84, 85, 86, 87
Domain: Number and Operations—Fractions			
Use equivalent fractions as a strategy to add and subtract fractions.			
5.NF.A.1	Add and subtract fractions with unlike denominators (including mixed numbers) by replacing given fractions with equivalent fractions in such a way as to produce an equivalent sum or difference of fractions with like denominators.	**5.NF.A.1**	Tier 1 Lessons: 52, 53, 54, 55, 56, 57 Tier 2/3 Skills and Activities: 11, 49, 53, 54, 55, 56, 57, 58, 59, 60
5.NF.A.2	Solve word problems involving addition and subtraction of fractions referring to the same whole, including cases of unlike denominators, e.g., by using visual fraction models or equations to represent the problem. Use benchmark fractions and number sense of fractions to estimate mentally and assess the reasonableness of answers.	**5.NF.A.2**	Tier 1 Lessons: 58, 59, 60, 61 Tier 2/3 Skills and Activities: 12, 16, 53, 54, 55, 56, 58, 59, 61, 62
Apply and extend previous understandings of multiplication and division to multiply and divide fractions.			
5.NF.B.3	Interpret a fraction as division of the numerator by the denominator *($a/b = a \div b$)*. Solve word problems involving division of whole numbers leading to answers in the form of fractions, mixed numbers, e.g., by using visual fraction models or equations to represent the problem.	**5.NF.B.3**	Tier 1 Lesson: 62 Tier 2/3 Skills and Activities: 38, 45, 55, 57
5.NF.B.4	Apply and extend previous understandings of multiplication to multiply a fraction or whole number by a fraction.	**5.NF.B.4**	
5.NF.B.4a	Interpret the product $(a/b) \times q$ as a parts of a partition of q into b equal parts; equivalently, as the result of a sequence of operations $a \times q \div b$.	**5.NF.B.4a**	Tier 1 Lessons: 63, 64, 65, 66 Tier 2/3 Skills and Activities: 22, 50, 52, 55, 57, 63, 64, 66

Intervention Resources

		Personal Math Trainer	Response to Intervention
5.NF.B.4b	Find the area of a rectangle with fractional side lengths by tiling it with unit squares of the appropriate unit fraction side lengths, and show that the area is the same as would be found by multiplying the side lengths. Multiply fractional side lengths to find areas of rectangles, and represent fraction products as rectangular areas.	**5.NF.B.4b**	Tier 1 Lessons: 68, 69 Tier 2/3 Skills and Activities: 32, 50, 55, 65, 67
5.NF.B.5	Interpret multiplication as scaling (resizing), by:	**5.NF.B.5**	
5.NF.B.5a	Comparing the size of a product to the size of one factor on the basis of the size of the other factor, without performing the indicated multiplication.	**5.NF.B.5a**	
5.NF.B.5b	Explaining why multiplying a given number by a fraction greater than 1 results in a product greater than the given number (recognizing multiplication by whole numbers greater than 1 as a familiar case); explaining why multiplying a given number by a fraction less than 1 results in a product smaller than the given number; and relating the principle of fraction equivalence $a/b = (n \times a)/(n b)$ to the effect of multiplying a/b by 1.	**5.NF.B.5b**	Tier 1 Lessons: 70, 71 Tier 2/3 Skills and Activities: 49, 66, 68
5.NF.B.6	Solve real world problems involving multiplication of fractions and mixed numbers, e.g., by using visual fraction models or equations to represent the problem.	**5.NF.B.6**	Tier 1 Lesson: 72 Tier 2/3 Skill and Activity: 65
5.NF.B.7	Apply and extend previous understandings of division to divide unit fractions by whole numbers and whole numbers by unit fractions.	**5.NF.B.7**	
5.NF.B.7a	Interpret division of a unit fraction by a non-zero whole number, and compute such quotients. For example, create a story context for (1/3) ÷ 4, and use a visual fraction model to show the quotient. Use the relationship between multiplication and division to explain that (1/3) ÷ 4 = 1/12 because (1/12) × 4 = 1/3.	**5.NF.B.7a**	Tier 1 Lesson: 74 Tier 2/3 Skills and Activities: 35, 51
5.NF.B.7b	Interpret division of a whole number by a unit fraction, and compute such quotients. For example, create a story context for 4 ÷ (1/5), and use a visual fraction model to show the quotient. Use the relationship between multiplication and division to explain that 4 ÷ (1/5) = 20 because 20 × (1/5) = 4.	**5.NF.B.7b**	Tier 1 Lessons: 74, 75 Tier 2/3 Skills and Activities: 35, 69, 51
5.NF.B.7c	Solve real world problems involving division of unit fractions by non-zero whole numbers and division of whole numbers by unit fractions, e.g., by using visual fraction models and equations to represent the problem. For example, how much chocolate will each person get if 3 people share 1/2 lb of chocolate equally? How many 1/3-cup servings are in 2 cups of raisins?	**5.NF.B.7c**	Tier 1 Lessons: 76, 77 Tier 2/3 Skills and Activities: 22, 35, 67, 70

Intervention Resources

		Personal Math Trainer	Response to Intervention
Domain: Measurement and Data			
Convert like measurement units within a given measurement system.			
5.MD.A.1	Convert among different-sized standard measurement units within a given measurement system (e.g., convert 5 cm to 0.05 m), and use these conversions in solving multi-step, real world problems.	**5.MD.A.1**	Tier 1 Lessons: 78, 79, 80, 81, 82, 83, 84 Tier 2/3 Skills and Activities: 7, 22, 24, 36, 83, 88, 89, 90, 91, 92, 93, 94, 95, 96, 97, 98, 99, 100
Represent and interpret data.			
5.MD.B.2	Make a line plot to display a data set of measurements in fractions of a unit (1/2, 1/4, 1/8). Use operations on fractions for this grade to solve problems involving information presented in line plots.	**5.MD.B.2**	Tier 1 Lesson: 85 Tier 2/3 Skills and Activities: 51, 61, 65, 70, 112
Geometric measurement: understand concepts of volume and relate volume to multiplication and to addition.			
5.MD.C.3	Recognize volume as an attribute of solid figures and understand concepts of volume measurement.	**5.MD.C.3**	
5.MD.C.3a	A cube with side length 1 unit, called a "unit cube," is said to have "one cubic unit" of volume, and can be used to measure volume.	**5.MD.C.3a**	Tier 1 Lesson: 87 Tier 2/3 Skill and Activity: 101
5.MD.C.3b	A solid figure which can be packed without gaps or overlaps using *n* unit cubes is said to have a volume of *n* cubic units.	**5.MD.C.3b**	Tier 1 Lesson: 88 Tier 2/3 Skills and Activities: 101, 104
5.MD.C.4	Measure volumes by counting unit cubes, using cubic cm, cubic in, cubic ft, and improvised units.	**5.MD.C.4**	Tier 1 Lesson: 89 Tier 2/3 Skills and Activities: 33, 105
5.MD.C.5	Relate volume to the operations of multiplication and addition and solve real world and mathematical problems involving volume.	**5.MD.C.5**	
5.MD.C.5a	Find the volume of a right rectangular prism with whole-number side lengths by packing it with unit cubes, and show that the volume is the same as would be found by multiplying the edge lengths, equivalently by multiplying the height by the area of the base. Represent threefold whole-number products as volumes, e.g., to represent the associative property of multiplication.	**5.MD.C.5a**	Tier 1 Lesson: 90 Tier 2/3 Skills and Activities: 22, 105
5.MD.C.5b	Apply the formulas $V = l \times w \times h$ and $V = b \times h$ for rectangular prisms to find volumes of right rectangular prisms with whole-number edge lengths in the context of solving real world and mathematical problems.	**5.MD.C.5b**	Tier 1 Lessons: 91, 92 Tier 2/3 Skills and Activities: 20, 103, 105, 106
5.MD.C.5c	Recognize volume as additive. Find volumes of solid figures composed of two non-overlapping right rectangular prisms by adding the volumes of the non-overlapping parts, applying this technique to solve real world problems.	**5.MD.C.5c**	Tier 1 Lesson: 93 Tier 2/3 Skills and Activities, 102, 106

Intervention Resources

		Personal Math Trainer	Response to Intervention
Domain: Geometry			
Graph points on the coordinate plane to solve real-world and mathematical problems.			
5.G.A.1	Use a pair of perpendicular number lines, called axes, to define a coordinate system, with the intersection of the lines (the origin) arranged to coincide with the 0 on each line and a given point in the plane located by using an ordered pair of numbers, called its coordinates. Understand that the first number indicates how far to travel from the origin in the direction of one axis, and the second number indicates how far to travel in the direction of the second axis, with the convention that the names of the two axes and the coordinates correspond (e.g., *x*-axis and *x*-coordinate, *y*-axis and *y*-coordinate).	**5.G.A.1**	Tier 1 Lesson: 94 Tier 2/3 Skill and Activity: 51
5.G.A.2	Represent real world and mathematical problems by graphing points in the first quadrant of the coordinate plane, and interpret coordinate values of points in the context of the situation.	**5.G.A.2**	Tier 1 Lessons: 95, 96 Tier 2/3 Skills and Activities: 113, 114
Classify two-dimensional figures into categories based on their properties.			
5.G.B.3	Understand that attributes belonging to a category of two-dimensional figures also belong to all subcategories of that category.	**5.G.B.3**	Tier 1 Lessons: 97, 98, 99 Tier 2/3 Skills and Activities: 107, 108, 110
5.G.B.4	Classify two-dimensional figures in a hierarchy based on properties.	**5.G.B.4**	Tier 1 Lesson: 100 Tier 2/3 Skills and Activities: 108, 109, 110

Name ____________________

Beginning-of-Year/End-of-Year Student Record Form

Item	Common Core Standard		Beginning-of-Year	End-of-Year
1	5.OA.A.1			
2	5.NBT.A.1			
3	5.NBT.B.6			
4	5.MD.C.5c			
5	5.NBT.A.3b			
6	5.NF.A.1			
7	5.NBT.A.2			
8	5.NF.A.2			
9	5.NF.B.4a			
10	5.NBT.A.3a			
11	5.NF.B.5a			
12	5.NF.B.3			
13	5.G.B.3			
14	5.OA.B.3			
15	5.G.A.1			
16	5.NBT.B.5			
17	5.NBT.A.4			
18	5.NF.B.7a			
19	5.NF.B.4b			
20	5.NBT.B.7			
21	5.NF.B.5b			
22	5.MD.B.2			
23	5.MD.C.3a			
24	5.NF.B.7b			
25	5.MD.C.3b			
26	5.MD.C.4			
27	5.MD.C.5a			
28	5.G.B.4			

Name ____________________

Middle-of-Year Student Record Form

Item	Common Core Standard		Middle-of-Year
1	5.NF.B.6		
2	5.NBT.A.1		
3	5.NBT.B.5		
4	5.MD.C.4		
5	5.NBT.A.3b		
6	5.NF.A.1		
7	5.NBT.A.3a		
8	5.NF.A.2		
9	5.NF.B.4a		
10	5.NBT.A.3a		
11	5.NF.B.6		
12	5.NF.B.3		
13	5.NF.B.4a		
14	5.NBT.B.5		
15	5.MD.C.3b		
16	5.NBT.B.5		
17	5.NBT.A.3b		
18	5.NF.B.4a		
19	5.NF.B.4b		
20	5.NF.A.1		
21	5.NF.B.4b		
22	5.MD.C.4		
23	5.MD.C.3a		
24	5.NF.B.6		
25	5.MD.C.3b		
26	5.MD.C.4		
27	5.MD.C.3b		
28	5.NBT.B.5		

Class Record Form

Name of Student									